The Fantastic Tails
of
Sammy and Mr. Chips

To
The Windham Public Library

D. A. Squires

Nov. 2018

The Fantastic Tails
of
Sammy and Mr. Chips

BY

D. A. Squires

Illustrations by Kelly Arnold

THIS BOOK IS INSCRIBED
TO
The Four Musketeers
Samuel Adams, Mr. Chips, Bud, and Ziggy

CONTENTS

"The time has come," the Walrus said,
"To talk of many things:
Of shoes—and ships—and sealing wax—
Of cabbages—and kings—
And why the sea is boiling hot—
And whether pigs have wings."

The Walrus and the Carpenter
Lewis Carroll

The Fantastic Tails
of
Sammy and Mr. Chips

PROLOGUE

If you have lived with a cat or a dog, you know they do not pay much attention to what you say.

Cats will typically feign complete disinterest until they hear the distinct sound of dry food tumbling from the bag, or the delicious swishing sound of the can opener, or the heavenly vacuum burst of a pop-top can. But the truth is, most cats are keen observers and listeners. Although they appear to be sleeping soundly during their frequent catnaps, if you look closely, one eye will usually blink open if someone in the house is talking.

Dogs, on the other hand (or paw), are far more interested in your Every Move. Should you fear you have lost your shadow like Peter Pan, you need only look down or nearby to know that you have not. They also *appear* to listen very well. However, this appearance is deceptive, because they are usually paying attention to *certain* words, unlike cats, who listen to the complete sentence.

Here is an example of how this works.

Think of the most boring teacher you ever had. Now imagine you have this teacher in the last class of the day and it's getting close to summer and the subject is Nutrition and all you can think of is how starving you are. And then you're daydreaming about a cheeseburger, maybe with bacon, when suddenly between the blah, blah, blahs you hear . . . your name. Loudly, with a "Mr." or "Miss" in front of it. Then something is said about the Principal's Office. The sensation is like an electric shock, and you sit straight up and try very hard to pay attention. This works for a little while, until the blah, blah, blahs once again have the same effect as a shot of Novocain. Now imagine the same classroom, but this time between the blah, blah, blahs you hear your name spoken by a choir of angels (maybe you have won the Academy Award for Best

PROLOGUE

Documentary about Nutrition), and something about the highest test grade and no homework. You are now listening, closely. It is called *selective hearing*, and both young people and dogs share this shortcoming (or skill, depending on your point of view). Simply stated, it is paying attention to certain words, not to the blah, blah, blahs. Of course, what matters most to both people and dogs is whether these words are *good or bad*.

VERY GOOD words for dogs: Treats, Cookies, Dinner, Ice Cream, Ball, Toy, Walk, or Ride. Upon hearing, they will burst out of their daydream, nap, or boredom and become instantly euphoric with eyes lit like sparklers and jet-propelled tails—the definition of Dog Bliss. However, if for some unknown reason they find themselves sitting in the Principal's Office for Dogs and words beginning with the letter *V* (as in Veterinarian or Vet, Vaccination, Visitor, Vacuum, or Vacation) are inexplicably and shockingly swirling through the air, well, if you have a dog, you know the reaction. These are VERY BAD words.

What follows are the fantastic tales (some tall, some true) of a cat named Samuel (aka "Sammy" or "Sam") Adams and a long-haired dapple dachshund named Mr. Chips. (There is another cat, but he is not adventurous and a little dimwitted, so he makes a somewhat brief appearance.) As told by the daring duo, with a little help from Mrs. S. (their mother) . . . and some good and bad words.

THE BEGINNING

T he morning began normally at Number Thirteen Rabbit Hill Road.

A weathered, oversized mailbox at the end of a dirt road was the only evidence that a house lay beyond. The red paint on the mailbox was faded, and the lettering of "Thirteen" was obviously hand painted, as was a large white rabbit with very long ears. One of the rabbit's ears was the flag to signal a letter was awaiting pickup. When raised, it appeared the rabbit was attentively listening for the sounds of the mail truck, and because one of the residents of Number Thirteen was an author, the white rabbit was listening quite often. Mostly, the postman delivered bills and other lackluster pieces of mail. But once in a blue moon, a letter arrived that made the rabbit smile (or this is what the author thought she saw). Beyond the mailbox, at the end of a long gravel driveway, sat a

3

rambling, time-worn colonial house, bordered by old stone walls and a meandering brook. The residence at the end of Rabbit Hill Road had settled into the hills of western Connecticut long ago, now as much a part of the land as the tumbledown stone walls.

Mr. S. was having breakfast and Mrs. S. was getting ready to go to work. This was not a long distance to travel—in fact, it was on foot, over a stone wall to a tiny one-room bungalow, which she called The Studio and Mr. S. called The Shed—where she wrote all day and then back over the stone wall for dinner. Occasionally, she would join Mr. S. for lunch, but not often. (She found it best to be by herself all day without any distractions.) Thankfully, Mr. S. was retired and took excellent care of the morning requirements of two cats and one dog, as well as the rest-of-the day requirements, whatever they might be. He made a healthy breakfast for himself every day, as he was quite health conscious, and without fail, shared the bottom of the yogurt cup with a dachshund named Mr. Chips. And if it was a cereal morning, also the remnants of milk with whomever was interested (usually all three at once, so this took some diplomacy and continual coaching on the subject of fairness, which did not seem to stick from one day to the next). Mrs. S. had her breakfast at work (lots of coffee). She was heading out the door when the first *V* word was spoken.

It was like the shot heard 'round the world.

"Don't forget to call the Vet today, we need to make the boarding arrangements . . . my poor musketeers, they won't like it at all—two weeks. We've never left them that long." Mrs. S. sighed. "Mr. Chips will be so sad, I wish we could take him with us, he has never been boarded . . . well, see you later, boys. Don't let Mr. S. get into trouble! Good-bye, Mr. Chips!" Mrs. S. grinned at the adorable two-year-old dapple dachshund (the dapple of her eye) and then she was out the door.

Samuel Adams, a gray and black striped cat with long legs (for a cat), swiveled to look at Mr. Chips, who appeared somewhat confused about what Mrs. S. had said. (Although he had clearly heard the word VET and knew about that: *not good*.) Sam arched one eyebrow, looking cool as always, the telegraphed message familiar: *we will talk about this, later*. When offered his morning treat, Mr. Chips was not his usual enthusiastic self, his brown eyes (with the whites showing) studying Mr. S. as he thoughtfully licked the bottom of the yogurt cup. A visit to the Vet was obviously on the horizon— would it be soon and for what . . . a shot? Questions flitted through his anxious mind and he shivered a tiny bit.

Mr. Chips was a major worry wart.

"Well, boys," said Mr. S., looking around at Sam, Bud (the other cat), and Mr. Chips, "looks like you'll be going on vacation when we do!"

Mr. S. smiled, but they all noticed he looked a little sad. Mr. Chips felt even more anxious. He had not heard the word VACATION in the two years he had resided at Number Thirteen Rabbit Hill Road and did not know what it meant. But it sounded ominous.

However, Sam and Bud knew the meaning. Very well. They were the first pets to live at Number Thirteen, and Mr. and Mrs. S. had taken what seemed like far too many vacations in those days. Sam had even given this period of time a name: "BC." Before Chips. After the dog's arrival, their only trips had been short Weekend Trips. It was unspoken, but both cats felt Mr. Chips had something akin to favored nation status because he always stayed with "The Lady Next Door," as she was called (even though her house was not within view), whereas the cats were carted off to the Vet. Frankly, it was impossible not to notice what could only be described as a strong whiff of favoritism wafting about the inside of a car that held two occupied cat carriers in the *back* seat and one dog on a leash in the *front* seat. Bud was never bothered by staying at the Vet—there was a lot of food (quantity being key, not quality) and fairly comfortable bedding—because sleeping and eating were his two favorite pastimes. He had no other interests. And he slept so soundly (usually snoring) that he never heard the racket around him. Whereas Sam had an entirely different reaction. He knew vacation meant a long time at the Vet's, cramped in a small space behind bars, bunked up with other cats and dogs who were usually crying or howling, which unfailingly gave him a bad headache. Sam prided himself on remaining calm in all circumstances, and found it irritating this was not a common trait among other felines or canines. For these reasons, he hated it when Mr. and Mrs. S. went on vacation. And this was the longest one ever. Two weeks. An eternity when you are a very smart cat.

Although, even by his own admission, Sam Adams had not used his vast intelligence that fine autumn day four years ago. A fateful day, one could say. He was a special cat, because he had been adopted as a kitten by a library called the Berkshire Athenaeum in Pittsfield, Massachusetts. And he had been given a prestigious name, Melville, after the famous author, Herman Melville, who wrote many of his books while living in the Berkshires. As the library cat, he had run of the place, everyone knew him, and he was the official mascot of the Melville Room, where he usually chose to nap. (He actually thought he was as famous as the author because people came to see him, his namesake being quite definitely dead.) Anyway, on that fateful day, he was outdoors scouting out a different place to nap when, on a whim (later much regretted), he hopped through the open window of a car parked in the parking lot and proceeded to fall asleep on the floor behind the driver's seat. When he awoke from a sound sleep, he was startled to find himself zooming along to the beat of a loud radio.

He had not noticed the car's Connecticut license plate.

Immediately upon assessing his predicament, he decided to lie low, never revealing his presence to the young driver, who obviously liked very loud music and speed. Eventually, they arrived someplace where the car stopped and the engine was turned off. Then the back door was opened to extract a duffel bag. Melville was inside (as luck would have it, the bag had been partially open and was not full). The young man lugged the bag into the house, dropping it off in a mud room just off the garage, leaving the inside screen door propped open when he went back outside. A small head poked out of the bag and cool green eyes surveyed the situation—the escape route was clear, and Melville did not waste a moment before making a mad dash to the nearby woods. Once hidden by foliage, the gray and black striped cat looked back at the young man, reflecting on what had happened in a moment of thoughtlessness (which was not like him), and then sauntered off into the hills of western Connecticut.

At first, he thought he could probably find his way back to the library, but as darkness fell, he had a strong intuition the Berkshire Athenaeum was not close by. At all. Nothing smelled or looked familiar. He had never travelled by car before, so he had no idea that a nearly two-hour drive translated into a long distance. Night fell and he was hungry and alone in a dark forest. He slept fitfully, burying himself in leaves. The next morning dawned early. He awoke to feel the emptiness of his stomach, the night's dampness on his fur, and an unfamiliar stiffness as he stretched.

It was the need for food that forced him to leave the relative safety of the woods for a nearby neighborhood. He had tried his best to nab a field mouse and then a small bird, but he was not skilled in the wild and his attempts were easily foiled. The house he happened upon was already occupied by cats (they appeared when he cried at the porch glass door, looking disdainful and unwelcoming, followed by a friendly dog who barked a pleasant greeting). Melville had had some experience with dogs—service dogs who accompanied their owners into the library. He decided he liked dogs, but the few cats he had met in his outdoor expeditions were not to his liking. Starving as he was, the bowl of milk set down on the porch was too delicious to ignore, and he had taken just a couple of laps when he was suddenly picked up from behind and pushed into a small crate with wires on the front and holes in the sides. The library cat was soon having the second car ride of his life, but this one was short. In no time, the crate was lifted out of the car and carried into a building. Conversations were brisk, and he was abruptly left at a place for pets with no homes. Melville had tried to protest, giving his name and where he was from; he even knew the street address and zip code of the Berkshire Athenaeum. All to no avail. They ignored him.

As luck would have it, about a week later Mr. and Mrs. S. decided Bud needed a cat friend. (Bud was often sullen, with a rather dull look in his eyes. What they didn't realize—he was a relatively new resident at Number Thirteen—was this was his natural state and friends would not change him.) They were peering into cages at the place for homeless pets, when their eyes locked onto a pair of green eyes that were very intelligent looking (for a cat). They read the bio: "Nickname from Staff: 'Cat Burglar.' Found abandoned in the area of Dark Woods. No ID or chip. Male, between two and three years old, excellent health. Has been well cared for. Presumed separated from owner. Seems to like dogs, not so much other cats, but might warm up. Has tried to break out of the cage every way possible, highly intelligent. To sum up: A cool customer."

Mr. and Mrs. S. looked at each other and smiled. The third car ride in about a week delivered the cool customer to Number Thirteen Rabbit Hill Road.

Melville strolled into the house, leisurely glanced around, and then methodically walked to each closed door. Standing up on his hind legs and reaching up with one very long front paw, he pulled down on the door handle with the dexterity of a person. Pushing the door open with his body, he walked in and thoroughly surveyed the room and its contents. Mr. and Mrs. S. stared at each other; this was a bit startling. Mr. S. then mumbled something under his breath about casing the joint, and Mrs. S. told him to shush, he was just getting the lay of the land. In fact, it did appear he was evaluating his new residence (and deciding if he liked it). Then he jumped up on every windowsill in the house and gazed out at each vista with the concentration of a land surveyor. They attempted to introduce Bud, but Melville seemed more interested in the house than the other cat. Bud just stared dully at his "new friend," as Mr. and Mrs. S. kept repeating in reassuring tones.

At dinner, they all watched the new resident eat and eat—*two* cans of delectable, gourmet cat food (Bud had observed this with great concern)—then wash himself and curl up on the rug staring at them as if asking, "What's next?"

"I like the name Samuel Adams. He looks very smart and somehow, wise. I think he should have an important historical name. Let's name him after one of the Founding Fathers. We can call him Sam or Sammy," said Mrs. S., most pleased with the idea. Then she smiled at the curled-up figure as though she assumed he understood what she said and would nod in agreement. (He did, but he did not nod in agreement.)

"Fine with me," replied Mr. S., with one eyebrow raised, "and we can keep the nickname Cat Burglar . . . or maybe Second-Story Sam . . . looks like he's going to have the run of the place."

Melville decided living with Mr. and Mrs. S. and their boring cat would be far less interesting than the Berkshire Athenaeum, but far, far better than the Dark Woods or the place for homeless cats and dogs. He knew something about the Founding Fathers, but he didn't think they were more famous than the author who wrote *Moby-Dick*. However, after turning it over in his mind for a while, he decided the new name would be okay.

This was how Samuel Adams (no longer Melville) came to live at Number Thirteen Rabbit Hill Road and how the household of Mr. and Mrs. S. came to have two cats (or musketeers).

VACATION PLANS

Mr. S. was out and about on the property, his usual morning routine after breakfast. (As he told them every day with the screen door banging shut behind him, "Out to survey the back forty, boys!" Whatever that meant.) Bud was trying hard to fend off sleep, stretched out on a thick pillowed chair, having this morning opted for the living room versus one of the upstairs beds covered with down-filled comforters. It was actually difficult to decide where to nap, because there were so many choices at Number Thirteen and not one was "off limits." Very, very nice when your earliest (but thankfully fading) memories involved drinking water from rain puddles, always being hungry and scrounging for garbage in alleyways, and being afraid day and night, which proved justified when someone very bad threw a rock at your head one dark and terrible night. Bud had no way of understanding that his limited attention span and lack of intellectual curiosity, what Sam called "His Everlasting Dullness," was caused by this dreadful event. But this morning, Bud was mildly interested in what Sam was going to tell the dog about *vacation,* so he had stayed nearby—if he could just stay awake and focused.

"Sammy, what is vacation?" asked a worried Mr. Chips, looking intently at Sam, the font of All Knowledge, as he had quickly learned upon becoming the third musketeer at Number Thirteen. Chips was lying on the braided rug, and Sam was sitting regally on a window seat.

Bud's eyes blinked open and Sam looked over at him knowingly. Then he returned his cool green gaze to the dog.

"Vacation means prison for pets. But you have never been to prison, Chips, so let me explain . . . you will be locked up in a small cell with some stale water and bad food and a thin bed. There are many other prisoners around you and most are hysterical. Crying, barking, it never stops, even at night. Dogs are walked twice a day in a narrow cement-walled run. No toys, no treats, no fun. Two weeks will seem like a year. You will definitely wonder if they will ever come back, or . . . if you have been *forgotten.* Bud and I know this, because before you were here, they used to go on a lot of vacations. For some reason, they have only taken Weekend Trips since you arrived. And . . . as you know, we go to the Vet while you stay in complete comfort with The Lady Next Door. So, now it's your turn to go to the Vet. What's fair is fair, right, Chips? Oh, and sometimes while you're there they give you shots, you know, *vaccinations,* the ones with the very long needles. Easy, because you are their *prisoner.*"

Chips felt tears flood his eyes and his body tremble with fear. This could not be possible. *Prison??*

"Is there any chance they won't go, Sammy?" Mr. Chips asked, his voice just a whisper.

"No, Chips. Mrs. S. is an author and this is a BIG DEAL trip. I've heard them talk . . . they're going to bookstores in Cape Cod and Maine. Far, far away from Number Thirteen."

Mr. Chips felt sick to his stomach and dazed all at once. It felt like his world was coming apart. What if Mr. and Mrs. S. did not return from vacation? What if they were left in prison for the rest of their lives? He looked mournfully and desperately at Sam Adams and then Bud, the whites of his eyes showing as he rolled them back and forth.

Bud looked back blankly, his yellow eyes showing no emotion. Contentedly sprawled on the thick chintz cushion, his tortoiseshell stripes and snowy white paws, chest, and belly were glistening in the morning sun. He was a very handsome cat, although overweight (from a strictly observed lack of daily activity and from eating Sam's uneaten portions regularly—Sam was lean and muscular and not a big eater, most fortuitous for Bud). Mrs. S. sometimes called him "Buddha Bud," a nickname that fit perfectly. Bud was large and rather majestic looking and often appeared to be in a meditative, gastronomically induced trance.

"It's not bad, Chips. Food dish is never empty. Cool in the summer and warm in the winter. And they have never forgotten us . . ." Bud said dully, offering his perspective (obviously living in an alternate universe from Sam's).

"Look, chaps, I've been thinking about this and I have a plan. Why don't we take a vacation when they do? It would be great fun—an adventure! Imagine all the places we'll see and interesting experiences we'll have?! The Grand Tour, as Mrs. S. would say! How about it?!"

Sam Adams looked like he was about to levitate with excite-ment. He was pacing back and forth on the window seat in deep thought, his tail up (a sweeping curve that looked like a question mark), and then he came to a stop and sat down. His long tail was now wrapped snugly around his body, twitching a little, and he looked at Bud and then Mr. Chips, smiling. Sam's smile had a mag-ical quality (sometimes a bit conniving, likely due to life experience and exceptional intelligence) and usually cast a spell over the young and impressionable Chips. However, this was never Bud's reaction, and it was clear he was glumly mulling everything over. It was a lot to absorb.

Predictably, the dapple dachshund's outlook had instantaneous-ly changed from inconsolable to effervescent.

"Yes!!! Let's go!!! Where are we going, Sammy?! How do we get there??"

Mr. Chips hopped around like a rabbit, as he always did when he was very happy and excited. Then he ran to his large basket filled with toys, found his current favorite stuffed animal, an orange and white striped monkey with long legs and arms and a still-very-good squeaker, (named "Monkey Business" by Mrs. S.), ran back to the window seat, and dropped it on the floor in front of Sam.

"I have to bring Monkey Business!!"

"Well, Chips, I'm happy to tell you that you may. We'll wear our backpacks that we got for Christmas, but we must pack lightly. This is going to be a hike and too much weight will slow us down," Sam answered, looking pleased to have been able to grant the request.

"A hike? How far?" asked Bud, obviously not enthused and immediately suspicious about the distance.

"I've been studying this map. I found it with the other maps Mr. S. keeps in his car."

Sam pulled out a rather yellowed map from behind a pillow with his teeth and then jumped down next to Chips and spread it out on the floor.

"The red X marks the spot where we are: Number Thirteen Rabbit Hill Road. See, Mr. S. wrote our address right here, where I made the red X . . . and we're not far from a road called Route 7," Sam said, as he traced one paw along the route.

"We'll just follow along Route 7 in the nearby woods until we come to State Parks. The parks are marked on the map with a large pine tree and Indian tepee. It's summer, so there will be a lot of campers and we can help ourselves to leftover food when they go to sleep. Camp under the stars, drink ice cold, fresh water from the streams, and make our way north as the sun shines . . ." Sam seemed to drift away in a reverie of happiness.

"North to where?" Bud asked, again without any genuine interest.

The question seemed to puncture Sam's reverie, and he now had a serious, faraway look in his eyes.

"The Berkshires. Just over the Connecticut state line. In Massachusetts," Sam answered quietly.

"I want to go back to where I was born and lived—for a while anyway."

The grandfather clock began chiming ten bells. The sound reverberated through the rambling house, a reassuring sound they were all accustomed to. When the last gong had drifted away, the silence continued for a moment, and then Sam's cool green gaze shifted back to Bud and Chips.

"I lived in a library. It has a fancy name, but means library. It's called the Berkshire Athenaeum. My name was Melville . . . after a famous author, Herman Melville. Mrs. S. sometimes mentions him, and she has his books in her studio . . . he died a long time ago. There's a special room in the library called the Melville Room. People came to visit me because, of course, they couldn't talk to him."

More silence. A lot to think about. Sam had never told them anything about his life before Number Thirteen.

"How did you get here? They said you came from the same place for orphan pets as I did?" Bud asked.

Bud seemed curious, for the first time Chips could ever remember.

"Hopped into an open car window and took a nap. Next thing I knew, I was far away in a strange place. You should try and remember this, Bud. *Watch where you nap*," Sam replied, sounding like a parent talking to a child, as he often did when talking to Bud.

Chips was trying to think about everything Sam said. It was all so unexpected and shocking. He had no memories before coming to Number Thirteen, none. And he was especially glad that he had no memories of the place for orphan pets. Then he thought of something that made his heart beat fast.

"Do you want to go back and . . . stay at the library?"

Chips was almost afraid to ask, but he had to know.

Sam Adams hopped back up on the window seat and sat down looking out the window. With his back to them, he answered.

"I have thought about it. I liked living there. The library was always . . . interesting. Books to read, new people every day, and

. . . I think I was famous. They wrote articles about me with my photo in *The Berkshire Eagle* newspaper. The Library Lady who fed me showed me the newspaper clippings, and she hung them up in the Melville Room. I guess I won't know until I get back. Maybe or maybe not."

Sam stood and turned around, gazing at them.

"But I want to go, and now is the time. For the Great Escape."

His green eyes shone with intensity as he studied Chips and then Bud.

"Are you going with me?"

THE GREAT (BUT NARROW) ESCAPE

Neither Bud nor Mr. Chips had answered right away.

In fact, they had no time because Mr. S. had come looking for Chips for his morning walk, Bud immediately fell sound asleep snoring, and Sam Adams took his morning constitutional, as Mr. S. called it—roaming the yard, hopping the stream, walking the stone walls, and last stop, checking on Mrs. S., where he usually took a catnap (short but very restorative, for people and cats). Listening to the clacking of the keys always put him right to sleep. Thankfully, it did not have the same effect upon the person doing the clacking.

It was later that night before Chips went to bed (another source of mild jealousy—he was allowed to sleep with Mr. and Mrs. S. and they were not) when Sam called a "Business Meeting."

"I need to know if we're going to be the Three Musketeers—what Mrs. S. always calls us—you know, all for one and one for all? Who's coming on the Grand Tour of Route 7 and Local Environs—destination the Berkshire Athenaeum?!" Sam asked, looking both expectant and confident of the answer.

No one answered.

Sam looked sternly at Chips.

"Well, then prison it is. Have fun, Mr. Chips."

"No, I mean yes, I'll go, Sammy. Are you coming, too, Bud?" Chips asked, looking hopefully into the blank yellow eyes. It just seemed like the more the better.

"Pass. I'll take prison." A long pause and then he continued, staring at Chips. "If I were you, Chips, I would find out how far your short legs are going to have to go. Regular meals and air conditioning might sound good . . ." Another long pause. "Once you know the distance."

Chips looked worriedly at Sam, who was staring at Bud. Maybe sneering was the better word.

"Bud, you should not try and influence the youthful and impressionable Mr. Chips. His decision to accompany me is very nice—what a good friend should do, for the once-in-a-lifetime journey back to one's roots. You may not have many memories of your beginnings, but that should not stop you from wanting to share this experience." Sam paused, looking at the turkey-sized silhouette. "Besides, you would lose some weight."

That insult was all it took. Bud turned his back on Sam and headed to the nearest soft cushion he could find. He was a definite NO.

"Well, Chips, it's just us. Two for the road! We have to pack tomorrow because they're leaving early the next morning. It's all going to work quite well. I'll tell you the plan tomorrow," Sam said, his voice filled with enthusiasm and confidence. It was obvious Bud's decision did not bother him.

They each headed to bed, one with gnawing fear in his stomach that would prevent a good night's sleep.

Chips tossed and turned all night. He had nightmares of pitch black woods, strange wild animal sounds, scary bonfires, strangers, being lost . . . it was *not* a restful night.

After breakfast, Sam called the next Business Meeting. Why he used that term was unclear to Chips. All he could think of was Monkey Business, which he immediately retrieved and brought with him to the meeting. Bud had disappeared to some soft bed upstairs.

"Tell me what you want in your backpack, Chips, and I'll pack it tonight after they go to bed. Not a lot, as I've said . . . I'll put a bag of the chicken-flavored cat treats we both like in my backpack, and just so you know the ground rules, they will be rationed. That means I decide who gets one and when. And I'm bringing the map and a small water bottle, just in case, and Mr. S.'s compass. So, what do you want in your backpack?" Sam asked, looking rather curious.

Chips first thought about Sam deciding who would get a treat. Probably okay, he was fair most of the time. Then he thought about what he needed in his backpack.

"Can I bring more toys, Sammy? I really like Rocky Raccoon and Herman the Hedgehog . . . I'm sure they would fit. And some of my bones and favorite cookies, and the blanket I like to sleep with, and my new raincoat and sweatshirt . . . and where are we going to sleep? Don't we need our sleeping bags and tent that we got last Christmas?" Chips asked hopefully. (He loved the small tent that Mr. S. set up for indoor camp-outs. Sam would usually sleep with him, but Bud said the sleeping bags weren't soft enough.)

The dapple face now had a worried look. There was more to this job of packing than met the eye (especially when you were young).

Sam Adams shook his head, realizing the packing part might present more of a challenge than he had anticipated.

"Chips, we have to pack light. Only the bare necessities. We have a long way to go . . ."

A long way to go . . . the words seemed to echo in his head and Chips was no longer thinking about his backpack.

"How far are we going, Sammy? Bud said my short legs might get tired. I only walk down Rabbit Hill Road with Mr. S. and we come right back. And then I take a nap," Chips replied, the worried tone unmistakable.

"It will take a few days, I think. But maybe longer. It's hard to tell from the map. We'll stop and rest whenever you want to, Chips. After all, we have two weeks to get there. And we're not walking back. The nice Library Lady will read our tags and call Mr. and Mrs. S. and they will come and get us—or you," Sam paused, wanting to be reassuring but also factual.

"And we can't take our sleeping bags or the tent, not enough room. Don't worry, Chips, we'll find good spots, out of the weather, there's always a porch or something we can crawl under if it rains. Now, let's get back to what you're bringing . . . I suggest one other toy, your choice, one bone, and one of Mrs. S.'s scarves, because your blanket won't fit. That's it. Okay, Chips?"

Chips had a hard time listening after the "*or you*" and generally found long conversations tiring. It was not easy to remember everything. But knowing he could not argue, he nodded and went to get Rocky Raccoon. The rest would be packed by the leader of the pack.

That evening after dinner there was another conversation.

"Chips, the other part of the plan I forgot to mention is the escape hatch. We'll leave through the cat door, which you have never been through before, even though I've invited you many times." Sam paused, recalling the many rebuffed invitations. It was cause for some concern. Chips was not the adventurous type.

"Anyway, they're leaving early tomorrow, right after breakfast, and The Lady Next Door is coming at 10 a.m. to take us to the Vet. You and I will have left by the time she gets here. So, have a good night's sleep and I'll see you in the morning—it's going to be the Grand Tour! A real vacation, not prison, remember that, Chips!" Sam smiled, his green eyes happy.

It was with a heavy, not happy, heart that Chips climbed the stairs to bed.

His last night at Number Thirteen Rabbit Hill Road.

He wondered how long it would be before he climbed the stairs again.

The next morning came early to a bleary-eyed Mr. Chips, who had again not slept well.

He made his way slowly down the stairs, preoccupied about the day ahead, when he was jarred out of his thoughts upon rounding the corner into the living room. There were *three* crates lined up in a row. He recognized the cats' crates immediately. The third and largest crate had to be for him, which was quickly confirmed when he spied Monkey Business on top. It was an unsettling sight and he felt his stomach twist.

However, it was what happened after breakfast that caused serious alarm (to one cat).

Mr. S. disappeared into the garage, returning with a piece of lumber and two brackets. In no time, he hammered both brackets into the wall and then slid the lumber inside the brackets. *Over the cat door*. He sat back on his knees, smiling at the neat job, and then grinned at the three spectators who were sitting nearby, staring. One in disbelief.

"This will do it, boys! No coons or other critters can move into Number Thirteen while we are away! The homestead will be safe and sound waiting for your return! Yep, no worries, Mr. Chips, your toys will all be accounted for, no one will play with them while the cats and dog are away! No, sir!" Mr. S. proclaimed as he stood up and admired his handiwork.

Soon, tearful good-byes were being said (with an inordinate number of hugs and kisses from Mrs. S.).

"The Lady Next Door will come for you soon . . . then it's off to the Vet! They will take wonderful care of you! See you in two weeks, my loves!!"

Mrs. S. took one last, lingering look at her three musketeers and then closed the door behind her.

Sam was already inspecting the reinforcement.

"Chips, come here, I think you can knock this up and out with your nose, standing in the middle. But just in case, Bud and I will push up on both ends on the count of three. Come over here, Bud. Sit down at that end and push up with your paws on the count of three," Sam said authoritatively, like a military officer directing his troops.

Very slowly, the overweight and lethargic recruit walked to one end. The commanding officer was at the other end, and the recruit with the long and powerful nose was in the center. (Chips was known to poke firmly and repeatedly when he wanted attention. Mr. S. humorously called it the "pigeon poke." The cats, however, were never amused.)

Then Sam counted down, "One, two, three!"

The lumber popped out quite easily and landed on the floor. Sam smiled, greatly relieved his plan had worked, and quickly headed to the living room. He hopped up on the crate for Monkey Business and efficiently stuffed the toy into Chips' backpack. Then he helped Chips get the neck harness over his head and pulled the two Velcro straps underneath the dapple torso with his teeth, securing them when Chips said they were comfortable. Next, he put on his own backpack and then put the lanyard attached to the compass around his neck (luckily, it fit perfectly). And at last they were ready—two musketeers off to see the world. (Or the part called Route 7 that wound northward from western Connecticut.)

Sam turned to face a sullen Bud.

"Are you sure you don't want to come? Just a few minutes to pack your backpack?"

Bud shook his head no and sauntered away.

"Okay, your choice, Bud," Sam said, shaking his head as he watched Bud hop up on a nearby chair. "The Library Lady will call Mrs. S. once we get there, she'll get the telephone number from our tags. So, hold down the fort at Number Thirteen, Bud."

The yellow eyes looked back at them, expressionless.

"Here we go, Chips, out where the birds fly free and so will we!"

Sam Adams had never looked happier. This was not how Chips was feeling.

"I'm out the door first and you're right behind!"

Sam pushed open the flap door and was out of sight in an instant.

Chips sat for a moment and looked around his house. Number Thirteen, his happiest place. He felt a lump in his throat and his eyes welled up. After a moment, he stood up and swallowed hard. Sam was waiting.

"Well, bye, Bud. I hope you have good time at the Vet's, or as good as it can be. See you again in two weeks," Chips said softly, and then he pushed the flap open with his nose. He did have to wriggle a little with the backpack; it was a narrow opening meant for cats, not small dogs with backpacks.

Then the flap door swished closed behind him and Chips was gone.

He did not hear Bud's whispered reply.

"Be safe, Chips."

FROM THE HORSE'S MOUTH

The morning was bright and sunny, not yet too warm, as Sam led the way through the woods—due west, he had determined (confirmed by periodically checking the compass). After a while they could hear the muffled sounds of cars and trucks whizzing by. Apparently, Number Thirteen Rabbit Hill Road was not too far from Route 7.

"Well, success, Chips! A good test of my map and compass reading skills, I would say!" Sam exclaimed, obviously quite pleased with himself as he turned to look at Chips.

"Are we almost there?" Chips asked, having found the backpack not really comfortable and the high grasses and rocky terrain not easy to negotiate. And he was a little out of breath. He noticed how easily Sam bounded up and around every little obstacle. Already it did not seem fair. This hike would be a lot easier if he was a cat.

"My good chap, Chips." Sam stopped to smile at the sound of "chap" and "Chips" and then continued.

"Patience and perseverance are going to be things you will need. A hike is not like a walk in the park. We have just begun the Grand Tour! We're going to follow Route 7, but stay out of sight in the woods. Because we do NOT want to attract attention, Chips. There seem to be a lot of people with small cages who are always on the lookout to trap cats and little dogs. So, add *beware* to patience and perseverance," Sam said, nodding knowingly at Chips, who looked a bit confused.

"What is perseverance?"

"That is sticking with something until you succeed. For example, let's say you lost Monkey Business somewhere in the house. You would not stop looking until you found him, right?"

Chips nodded.

"So, that's what you need to think about. We have to keep going until we get to our destination, even if it takes some time, okay, Chips?"

Of course, the truth was, Sam had no idea how long it would take. But his pep talk seemed to work, and Chips trotted along behind him (at least this was now pretty level ground) and soon they were making good progress heading north (again confirmed by the compass). They stopped for short breaks here and there, and soon it was time for a longer break and some food.

"Let's stop here, by this stream, Chips."

Chips nodded eagerly in agreement and headed to the stream and drank and drank. The water did taste especially good, fresh and cold. Then Sam had a drink (he was clearly not as thirsty) and took off his backpack and pulled out the cat treat bag, studying the front of the package.

"It says there are thirty treats in the bag. So, let's agree to two a day for each of us. That would be four per day total, and I'm sure we won't eat all of them before we get there."

Chips nodded, but all he could think of was JUST TWO? At home, Mr. S. (when Mrs. S. was at work) usually dumped out a small pile and it was every cat and dog for himself. Somehow, Bud always managed to be very fast in spite of his weight, pouncing faster than a speeding bullet and inhaling the treats like a high-powered vacuum. But Chips usually managed to get three or four, sometimes more if Mr. S. became distracted and kept pouring. Those were very good days.

"Do you want two now, or one now and one later?" Sam asked, with some curiosity as to what the answer would be.

Chips thought hard. He was hungry from all the walking and felt like he could easily eat the whole bag, in about one second.

"What are you going to do, Sammy?"

Sam studied him and then said, "One now. One before bed."

Chips decided this was a good idea, and nodded his agreement. But the mention of bed made him think of nighttime and where they would sleep, and he shivered.

Ripping open the tab with his sharp teeth, Sam dipped one paw into the bag and pulled out two treats. Very ceremoniously, he pushed one treat toward Chips and waited. It was obvious he wanted Chips to eat first. Chips stared at the teeny tiny treat lying in the grass and wondered if it was all he would eat that day. He remembered something about campsites and leftover food, but they had not come across a single campsite all morning. His stomach was making noises and he felt the saliva drooling from his mouth. When he could not wait a moment longer, he inhaled the miniscule treat (just like Bud). It tasted like he had eaten air—there was no taste at all. Then Sam ate his treat, very slowly. He chewed deliberately with delicious crunching noises and finally swallowed with great gusto, licking his lips.

"Just a suggestion, Chips, to eat more slowly, like Mrs. S. is always telling you. And now that we have, um, limited rations, this would be a good thing to remember."

Chips furrowed his brow and thought. Sam was always telling him what to do and giving him too much to remember. The Grand Tour was not starting out to be a lot of fun.

They made steady progress, never coming across anyone—person or animal (other than some squirrels and birds)—and it was now late in the afternoon. Sam decided it was time to get his bearings, and they stopped so he could look at the map to locate the nearest campsite. According to the map, there was a pine tree and tepee in a town called Sharon and a campground called Housatonic Meadows, located right next to Route 7. Sam knew they had not passed it, but he did not know how far away Sharon was. And night was coming. And they were both *very* hungry.

"Are we almost to the campground where there are leftover hot dogs and hamburgers, and maybe some watermelon?" Chips asked hopefully, dreaming about a platter of his favorites. (He LOVED watermelon.)

Sam did not answer right away, and now his brow looked furrowed.

"I don't think we'll get there before nightfall. Just a guess, but I'm beginning to think this map is not very accurate. It seems like we should already be in Massachusetts—look here, Chips."

Sam traced his paw over what looked like four inches on the map—from X marks the start at Number Thirteen to the Berkshire Athenaeum (Sam had made another large red *X* next to Pittsfield). Chips studied the map and had to agree, but there was a much bigger concern on his mind.

"Sammy, where are we going to . . . eat . . . and sleep?"

Sam was still studying the map and did not answer right away.

"Maybe this is a very old map . . . there are tepees on the map . . . maybe it's from the time the Indians lived here. Now that I think about it, remember how Mrs. S. always asks Mr. S. if he has checked the map before they go anywhere, and how she says they usually get lost anyway? Maybe it's because he has old maps . . ."

Sam turned to Chips, who now looked quite despairing.

"What are we going to do, Sammy?! Maybe we should turn back . . . we could go to The Lady Next Door and ask her to take us to the Vet? We would be with Bud, and I know it's like prison, but at least it's safe and Bud said there's always a lot of food . . ." Chips' voice was higher pitched than normal and he was talking unusually fast.

"Chips. NO. Remember? Perseverance, never giving up. We just need to find some food and a safe place to sleep and find out where we are. Now, let me think . . ."

Chips slumped down, flat as a flounder, his back legs straight out behind him, the backpack a little askew. The whites of his eyes reflected glum resignation—his plan had been rejected, and no appeal would be heard.

Suddenly, they both heard a horse neighing and stomping the ground in the distance. Sam brightened and stood up.

"Here we go, Chips, someone we can talk to . . . I'm sure he will help us. Cheerio, Chips, onward to the horse!"

Chips could not believe it. Sam thought a horse would help them? He had seen horses on Rabbit Hill Road. On their walks,

Mr. S. often stopped at a neighbor's barn and fenced paddock. The horses paid no attention to him, only to Mr. S., and they never even said hello, not a word.

Sam had hurriedly put on his backpack and was already headed in the direction of the horse, so Chips got up and ran after a him. Soon they emerged from the woods into a grassy field with white fencing. And there was the horse, standing next to the fence.

"Hello there! Any chance we could ask for some help? We're travelling through the area and have lost our bearings . . . map's a bit old . . . say, what's your name? Mine is Samuel Adams, but you can call me Sam or Sammy, and this is Mr. Chips, you can drop the 'Mr.,' Chips is just fine."

Sam looked at Chips, who scowled back at him. Sam only occasionally used his full name, having dropped the "Mr." a long time ago.

The horse was clearly studying them. He was very handsome, chestnut brown with a white star (that's what it looked like) on his forehead.

"Where are you from?"

Chips was shocked—a horse who talked.

"Western Connecticut, near Route 7," Sam replied, in a world-weary, cat-about-town voice.

The horse smiled, his gigantic teeth on full display, and then he began to laugh. The sound was a little odd, like laughing and neighing, mixed together.

"Well, I am sorry to inform you, Samuel Adams, that is where you still are."

Now the horse was laughing hard.

Sam was in shock, insulted, and angry, all at once.

Chips could not believe it. They had made no progress and they had walked all day??

"The name is Star, after my white mark. Now, don't be mad, I couldn't resist. You are obviously not . . . seasoned travelers. Maps are drawn to scale . . . that means you cannot look at a map and know how long it will take to get somewhere. Come along, boys, I'll get you some grub and you can sleep in my barn. We'll talk about where you are headed. I know this area very well. Horses get around, as you might expect."

Star's big brown eyes were kind and sparkly, reflecting his sense of humor. Then he turned and trotted toward a large red barn.

Followed by a happy dog and an embarrassed cat, all because of what had come—from the horse's mouth.

THE BARN

S tar led them into the barn.

It was airy and spacious and reminded Chips of Number Thirteen, because the barn felt homey and safe. Suddenly, he felt the first real twinge of homesickness, but it passed quickly because there was so much to look at. He had never been in a barn before.

There were a couple of horse stalls and a loft stacked with hay bales. A tall wooden ladder was propped against one part of the loft flooring. In one corner of the barn there were all kinds of tools hanging on the wall, and in another area, tractors and farm equipment. It all looked very organized and neat, not what Chips thought the inside of a barn would look like. The air had a kind of sweet, earthy smell, nothing he had ever smelled before, but he liked it.

"Welcome, Sam Adams and *Mr.* Chips, to Blueberry Hill Farm! Make yourselves at home. You can bunk in the stall next to mine tonight. The occupant is away, competing in some jumping competitions. Her name is Sapphire. I'm sorry you won't meet her. Very beautiful *and* talented. Over there, on the wall, are her ribbons." Star was looking proudly at the bulletin board filled with mostly blue ribbons, and then he turned to face them.

Chips decided he really liked this horse. *Mr.* Chips.

"Won't be long before you'll meet some of the other residents of the farm. They always come into the barn late in the afternoon . . . there's Beeeeeezly, he's a bloodhound. Only problem is, his nose doesn't work well anymore, so he doesn't go hunting like he used to and that makes him ornery. And Buttercup, she's a pig. Smarter than Beeeeeezly and a little bossy. They both eat their meals in the barn, so you'll get something to eat, unless you like oats? I have lots of oats and happy to share?"

Star was hoping oats might appeal, knowing Buttercup did not like the word "share."

Sam Adams had been listening, but at the same time he was surveying the barn. He was immediately interested in the ladder and the loft, and was heading over to it when he answered.

"Very hospitable of you, Star. Mind if I take a look at the upstairs?"

Before Star could answer, Sam was on his way up the ladder, with the ease of a fireman.

"Have a look, Sam, but it's only hay as far as I know."

Chips was sitting down, trying to absorb the fact that he would be meeting some kind of hound dog and a pig and hoping they were friendly and wondering how much of their dinners they would share. Because he was sure he would not like oats. And he wondered why the horse stretched out the dog's name when he said it—Beeeeeezly. But then again, he was still adjusting to a horse who could talk (and laugh) and how deep the horse's voice was and how big his teeth were. He was used to cats talking, but a talking horse took some getting used to, and the way he said the dog's name, it was all kind of funny.

Then Sam began speaking from his perch high atop a stack of hay bales in the loft. It made Chips dizzy just looking up at him.

"Yes, I can report it's only hay up here! Always nice to know what's above you before going to sleep. Just a habit of mine . . . oh, and about dinner. Chips and I will pass on the oats, but thank you for offering, Star."

Sam proceeded to climb down the ladder, as easily as he went up. Chips was imagining Sam wearing a fire hat and yellow raincoat and thinking he should have been a firehouse cat, not a library cat. Chips believed that Sam Adams could do anything he set his mind to. Anything.

The explorer hopped off the last rung of the ladder and then sauntered into Sapphire's stall. Chips followed. It did look quite cozy. There was a lot of hay piled in one corner, which looked soft and pretty comfortable. Almost like a bed, Chips thought.

"Take off your gear, gents! Believe me, I know how good it feels not to have anything on your back!" Star said cheerfully, as he watched them from the end of the stall.

Sam seemed to think a moment and then, deciding it would be okay, helped Chips out of his backpack and did the same for himself. Star was right, it felt so good to Chips. Even though the backpack wasn't heavy, he was not used to having anything on his back.

Just as they were stowing their backpacks in the stall, they heard the commotion. A deep, reverberating hound bark, then the pattering of feet, followed by a strange noise that sounded like a loud snort.

"Here they come . . . follow me and I'll introduce you . . ." Star said as he moved away from the stall.

Chips looked worriedly at Sam. A hound dog and a pig would be bigger than he was, and what if they weren't as nice as the horse? Chips knew Sam could escape up the ladder, but he certainly wouldn't be able to follow. Sam seemed to be reading his mind.

"It'll be okay. Star is friendly, I'm sure they will be, too. Come on, Chips, let's go . . . and remember to be very, very polite because they are our meal ticket . . . so to speak."

For some reason Chips found this confusing and a little worrisome—who would be whose meal ticket?

Sam led the way out of the stall, tail straight up with the question-mark curve, now most appropriate given the circumstances. Chips reluctantly followed, his handsome fan tail (that looked like a waving flag when he was happy) now dusting the floor.

There they were, the hound and the pig. BIG as life. Especially the pig. Buttercup was gigantic. She was very pink, her large nose appeared to be wet (and not very attractive), and her small, beady eyes seemed to be sizing them up. The dog was big-boned and lanky, with droopy, sad eyes and saggy folds of skin around his face, and very long, flappy ears. Beezly looked harmless, even somewhat depressed. Buttercup had the unmistakable look of "I am very smart and can run faster than you might think, so tread carefully because I am really a pink-skinned bull."

"Let me make the introductions: Beeeeeezly and Buttercup, please make the acquaintance of Sam Adams, the cat, and Mr. Chips, the dog." Star smiled with his teeth showing, and then added, "And vice versa. I hate long introductions."

Then Star laughed at his own remark, and it did seem to cut the tension.

"They're just passing through and they'll sleep in Sapphire's stall tonight. We'll find out where they're headed after dinner. I know you'll both be polite to our guests and leave some of your food for them, because they don't like oats."

Star directed his last comment to Buttercup, but she did not look at him. She was staring at Sam and Chips with a very unhappy (perhaps more accurately angry) expression. Chips could easily imagine her suddenly charging, with steam coming from her large nostrils, and he and Sam running for their lives. He instinctively took a few small steps backwards.

"Nice to meetcha," Beezly said, his voice as tired sounding as he looked.

Chips and Sam both swiveled from Beezly to Buttercup.

She seemed to be standing her ground. In other words, not ready to greet them. Or share her dinner.

Then she looked up at Star with a disgruntled stare.

"Buttercup, please greet our *guests.*" Star's large brown eyes shone with intensity.

It was a stare down. Like a contest. And who was going to win, Star or Buttercup? Chips felt his heart racing, suddenly realizing he was no longer hungry. And when that thought popped into his head, he found himself speaking (nervously and high-pitched).

"Ummm, excuse me . . . you don't need to leave anything for me, Buttercup. Nope, I'm fine. Had a cat treat earlier today and I'm still not hungry!" Chips chirped, feeling relief, almost happiness, course through his small body. Surely this was the right thing to say and all would now be well with Buttercup.

Sam turned to stare at Chips in disbelief. Star was also looking at him, with something like surprised disappointment. All the good feelings disappeared.

Buttercup was also looking at him with a completely different expression: approval.

"*Very nice* to meet you, Mr. Chips," Buttercup said in a raspy voice that was not warm, but not cold either.

All of a sudden there was another sound, a man whistling, and he was approaching the barn.

"Quick, both of you into Sapphire's stall. Get under the hay, just in case."

Star's voice was urgent, and both Sam and Chips nearly dove into the stall and were under the hay in seconds.

The man kept whistling and they could hear food being poured into bowls, and then the man left.

"Coast is clear, come on out!"

Star was looking at the pile of hay from the open end of Sapphire's stall as two heads poked through and then they emerged, pieces of hay clinging to their fur. Sam casually walked back into the barn. Chips sat in the doorway of the stall. It felt safer.

Both Beezly and Buttercup were now eating. The bloodhound was sitting, kind of slung to one side, leisurely chomping away, his long ears hanging down into the bowl. The pig was making contented snorting sounds between each huge, ravenous bite. Wafting from her enormous dish were the delicious aromas of bacon, beef stew, roast turkey, and buttermilk biscuits, or that was what Chips thought he smelled.

His stomach began to growl, the emptiness almost painful.

"Happy to leave some grub, fellas. Sorry, Sam, it's dog food . . ."

Beezly stepped away from his bowl and Sam bellied up—quickly. Chips watched as Sam ate. He was eating like Beezly, slowly savoring the food, casting a few "I don't feel sorry for you" looks over his shoulder at the woeful Chips. He leisurely licked the bowl *clean* and then sashayed away to wash himself.

Buttercup continued to snort and sigh, smacking and licking her lips with gusto. It took a while before she stepped away from her bowl and then she slowly headed for some hay in one corner of the barn. Chips watched her. She looked more rotund (if that was possible) than before the meal. Having short legs himself, he wondered how her tiny legs could support all that weight.

The dinner drama over, Star walked into his stall and began eating his oats in peace.

Which left Chips sitting in the doorway of Sapphire's stall, starving, but already knowing there was going to be no change to that feeling foreseeably. With a deep sigh, he crept back into the hay and tried to go to sleep. Eventually he fell asleep, for how long he didn't know. Chips was roused by a raspy voice.

He was looking into Buttercup's face. Close. Her large pink nostrils were inches from his face and he could feel her warm breath. It was a shocking sight and fear paralyzed him. In sheer panic, he thought, *she is still hungry . . . and I am her next meal ticket, what Sammy had said.* He was about to yelp when he began to hear what she was whispering.

". . . I left you some scraps at the bottom of my bowl. Some bacon and beef stew. Go and eat, Mr. Chips."

It was later that night, under one dim light left on in the barn, when they all gathered to look at the map, Beezly, Buttercup, Star, Sam, and Chips.

A feeling of comradery had sprung to life once it became known Buttercup had done the polite thing after all. Everyone was

happy—and full. However, it then became clear that once fed, the residents of Blueberry Hill Farm had very definite (and differing) opinions.

"Blueberry Hill Farm is NOT in Canaan, Connecticut, Beeeeeezly. It's in Kent, Connecticut," Star said emphatically.

Star was stamping his hoof at this point, because Beezly kept telling Star he was wrong. Beezly had been quite the hunting dog in his youth, but now age and dimness of mind were catching up with him. He was easily confused, but this only made him hold more stubbornly to his opinions.

"I am going to put an end to this right now. We live in Kent, Beezly, Star is right. I've seen the *Kent Good Times Dispatch* newspaper delivered here too many times not to know that fact. Besides, I know they buy the delicious eggs and bacon from the Kent Market. I've seen the name on the grocery bags. Something I am personally interested in and thankful for . . . because they are the BEST eggs and bacon," Buttercup said with great authority.

Her eyes had a superior, "do not argue with me" look, as she stared at Beezly.

Beezly took a moment to think about what Buttercup said. She did know the inner workings of the household, because she had become their pet instead of their bacon many years ago. The lady of the farm had taken a liking to her and, realizing how intelligent she was, allowed her to come and go (*in the house*) as she pleased. But it was the day she was given her name, Buttercup, that Beezly knew for certain she would be a resident of Blueberry Hill Farm. No one would name someone and then eat them. Beezly also thought it was rather bizarre Buttercup loved bacon. However, he realized she probably didn't know bacon came from pigs. And he was not going to tell her.

"All right, Kent," Beezly said, scowling at the pig.

"Glad that's settled. Now, looking at *X* marks the start, you boys began your trip somewhere near New Milford. You did well for the first day, but the truth is, you still have a *very long way to go* to get to Pittsfield, Massachusetts, on the hoof, if you'll pardon the expression," Star said with a smile, but there was obvious concern in his voice.

A very long way to go. Chips was once again deflated, like a balloon slowly losing its air. They could turn around tomorrow and make it back to Number Thirteen by nightfall. But how to convince Sam?

"Wait, what day is it tomorrow? Don't you go to the paddock in North Canaan for your workout tomorrow? You go every Thursday, Star," Buttercup said, once again proving her smarts.

"That's right! Perfect! You can ride along in the horse trailer and slip out when no one's looking once we get there! Buttercup, you are a true porcine genius!" Star grinned at the pig with his big teeth, and Buttercup seemed to become pinker with the compliment. "North Canaan is very close to the Massachusetts border!"

CHAPTER FIVE

Sam looked at the map. Star was right. The ride would be a big, big help. Sam relaxed and stretched, glancing at Chips.

It was obvious Chips had mixed feelings.

"Once we get to the border, how far is it going to be?" Chips asked, looking up into Star's large brown eyes. Star definitely knew more about maps than Sam.

"Well, Mr. Chips, I would say it's going to take some *horsepower* to get to your destination," Star answered, grinning with his big teeth. "But if you can hitch a ride or two, here and there, it shouldn't take that long. Something will work out . . . you found Blueberry Hill Farm by accident, so don't worry. And the trip is important. Sam Adams should get back to his real home."

Sam had explained the reason for the trip when he first showed them the map, and they all agreed he should return to where he came from. Beezly said, "Nothin' like the comforts of home." Buttercup said, "Home is where your heart is and where your stomach is never empty." And Star said, "Home is where you belong."

Chips had, of course, agreed with what they said. But he felt like Sam already had a real home at Number Thirteen, and it worried him (a lot) that Sam might choose to stay at the library. He was remembering all of this when he heard Sam's voice.

"Let's get some shut-eye, Chips, who knows what tomorrow's adventures will bring! At least we know we'll be in Massachusetts by nightfall. Great piece of good luck, seems like a good omen for the rest of the Grand Tour. Come along, Chips!" Sam's voice was happy and confident as he headed for Sapphire's stall.

Chips was still worried. What if there were no rides and they had to walk the whole way? What if no one wanted to share their food? It all felt so uncertain, nothing like the wonderful routine at Number Thirteen. He had never worried about anything living with Mr. and Mrs. S.

The barn was quiet. No one spoke for a while. A moth fluttered around the dim light and crickets were making their nighttime cacophony. Loud, but somehow soothing. It was the sound of summer.

"Mr. Chips, I can promise you a nice breakfast. I will leave a bit more at the bottom of my bowl."

Buttercup looked almost angelic to Chips, her pinkness glowing in the dim light.

"Thanks, Buttercup," Chips replied softly. "See you in the morning."

Chips got up and headed to bed.

OVER THE RIVER
AND THROUGH THE WOODS

Chips crept into Sapphire's stall and headed for the pile of hay. As he got closer, he stopped as his eyes adjusted to the darkness.

Mrs. S.'s scarf was draped across the hay. And lying on it was . . . Monkey Business.

Sam was sound asleep, curled up in the fragrant straw next to the scarf.

They were far from Number Thirteen and heading farther away the next day, but Sam was trying to make him feel at home. Chips lay down on the scarf and breathed in the faint smell of her perfume. Tears came into his eyes as he pulled Monkey Business under his chin and tried to go to sleep.

There was something about farm life that Star had neglected to mention. Roosters.

The next morning (very early, the sun barely up) came early and loudly.

Sam and Chips bolted out of their sound sleep staring at each other, then crept out of the warm hay bed and stood at the doorway of Star's stall. Star was wide awake, looking at two perplexed faces (one carrying an orange and white monkey in his mouth).

"Maybe I forgot to tell you . . . on a farm you can never sleep late. Never. But the good news is, gents, the grub will soon be here, along with Beeeeeezly and Buttercup. So, just lie low until you hear the whistling come and go, and then we can have breakfast. And, very glad Buttercup finally remembered her manners yesterday, Mr. Chips," Star said, smiling at Chips.

Chips nodded happily, and Sam led the way back into Sapphire's stall to await the whistling.

Star certainly knew the routine at Blueberry Hill Farm. Like clockwork, the whistling came and went, and soon they were all assembled in the main area to watch the first shift eat, followed by the second shift. Buttercup proved good for her word. When Chips looked down, there was a good inch of cheesy scrambled egg, bits of toast with jam and butter, sausage, and gravy. It was the best breakfast Chips had ever had. Mr. and Mrs. S. were quite health conscious, which translated into food that was *nutritious*, but in truth, not *delicious*. As he licked the empty bowl for about the tenth time, he looked over at Buttercup and wondered if a dog had ever fallen in love with a pig. He now understood how that could happen.

Sam washed up, the backpacks were strapped on, and in no time, they were ready. Star explained how this would work, The Plan, as he called it: they would wait until he was loaded into the horse trailer, and when the coast was clear, they were to run up the ramp into the trailer and hide under the hay. Once at the destination, they would wait until he was unloaded and then make a dash for the nearby woods. Simple. But not really. Star said the timing had to be perfect—getting into and out of the trailer without being seen and *before* the trailer door was closed. If they were seen, Star said someone might try and trap them. Sam knew about traps, so he paid very close attention to this warning.

It was not long before they had to say their good-byes.

Chips felt much sadder than he expected to. Even though he had just met them, it was suddenly hard to say good-bye. He felt like they were his friends, and he knew he would miss them.

"Well, good-bye, Mr. Chips. I wish you and Sam Adams safe travels and good food. If you're ever back this way, I hope you will stop and visit." Buttercup's raspy voice was soft. She had very long, attractive eyelashes (Chips had noticed this when her face was so close to his), and the long lashes now covered her lowered eyes. Then she looked up.

"There will always be some scraps in my bowl for you, Mr. Chips."

Chips felt tears come into his eyes.

"Thank you, Buttercup. For sharing. I really hope I'll see you again, someday."

Then Sam said his good-byes and Beezly said his, and soon they were crouched behind a bush, waiting for the right moment to make a mad dash into the trailer. The warm feelings had disappeared and Chips now felt nervous. He was hearing the word "trapped" silently repeat in his head. Sam's steady green eyes were astutely assessing the situation, watching everything.

Suddenly, Sam whispered, "Run. Now. Right behind me, Chips!"

They were like two streaks, skidding to a stop underneath Star's massive body and then diving under a pile of hay.

"Good job, gents! I'll let you know when we arrive."

The trailer began moving and they were on their way to North Canaan, one horse and two stowaways. The ride was bumpy and noisy. Wind was coming through small open windows and the road noise was reverberating inside the trailer, so conversation was not possible. Chips found himself staring up at the massive size of Star, his long muscular legs and powerful chest. Riding with Star made him feel protected and safe, and he wished they could go together in the noisy trailer all the way to the library.

It seemed like the ride took a long time, another troubling thought for Chips. They would need more rides, Star had said, but just as he started to worry about how they would find rides (and with whom), his thoughts were interrupted.

"Okay, gents, here we are at the track, heading for the paddock. Make a dash as soon as I'm out of the trailer, once the coast is clear. Hope you'll visit us again, it's Blueberry Hill Farm in KENT, easy to remember unless your name is Beeeeeezly. Best of luck, and happy homecoming, Sam Adams!" Star said softly, as the trailer was coming to a stop.

"Thanks for everything, Star. Your hospitality will not be forgotten," Sam replied, the respect and appreciation evident in his voice.

"Thank you, Star. I really liked meeting you and Beeeeeezly and Buttercup . . . and I hope we'll visit your farm again . . . someday," Chips said softly, pronouncing Beezly that way Star always said it.

"You're both welcome," Star replied, and then he grinned at Chips with his large teeth. "When you leave the trailer, head for the woods. Route 7 is just beyond. And Sam, be sure to check your compass now and again. Heading is due north. That's easy to remember, too."

The compass was around Sam's neck, and Sam looked up and nodded. As the trailer came to a stop, Sam and Chips buried themselves in the hay out of sight. Minutes later, the trailer door was being opened and the handsome horse with a star on his forehead leaned over and whispered, "Happy trails, gents."

Sam waited a few minutes and then crept to the open end, on the lookout for any people. No one was in sight, so he waved his paw and Chips scurried to his side. Then they were out of the trailer and running to the nearby woods—flashes of black, gray, and brown—unseen by anyone except some birds.

The weather was again cooperating: blue skies with a few wispy clouds. It was a warm day, but cooler in the woods. Sam checked the compass and assured Chips they were heading north, and the traffic noise on Route 7 was within earshot. Their stomachs were full, they felt well rested, and the day looked promising as they moved along at a good clip.

The Massachusetts border was next.

About noon time, Sam called for a break, which Chips had been ready for about an hour earlier, but had not requested, remembering patience and perseverance.

"This looks like a good spot to rest and have our first treat," Sam said, surveying the woodsy area, which looked quiet and safe.

Sam adeptly took off his backpack and opened the cat treat bag, doling out one treat for each of them.

This time, Chips was careful about how he ate the treat. He first swept it up on his tongue, let it melt a little in his mouth (delicious), and then moved the fast disappearing morsel over to his molars and carefully bit down. The tiny treat disappeared, but the taste lingered, and he knew this was the way he would eat cat treats from now on.

Sam watched Chips with approval, and then he leisurely ate his treat.

"Sammy, how are we going to know when we cross the border into Massachusetts? Is there a fence we have to go through?" Chips asked. He had been wondering about this.

"We're going to have to read some of the road signs. I assume there is a very big welcome sign, maybe with flashing lights. I don't think there's a fence, but if there is, I'm sure we can squeeze through, small door experts that we are," Sam answered with a conspiratorial smile.

"Star said we would be close to the border . . . what if we missed the sign?" Chips asked, remembering Star's words and feeling worried.

Sam was lying on his back, chewing on a long blade of grass.

"I don't think we missed it, but we'll keep an eye out for the next road sign." Sam paused as another thought came into his head.

"And Chips, we're going to have to look for a good place to stay overnight. The map doesn't show any nearby campgrounds."

Chips felt his stomach twist. He knew there was very little chance they would find another Blueberry Hill Farm.

CHAPTER SIX

It was not long after they resumed hiking alongside Route 7 when they found out they were already in Massachusetts. One sign read, "Entering Sheffield, Massachusetts," and another said, "Visit Historic Covered Bridge—Ahead One Mile." The next sign said, "Appalachian Trail Intersection Ahead." Sam pulled out the map to confirm they were now in Massachusetts and to get their bearings.

"YES, we're now in Massachusetts, Chips!! And looks like we have a choice. We could hike on the Appalachian Trail for a while or stay closer to Route 7. The hiking trail looks interesting, and I'm sure we'd meet a lot of hikers with . . . food. What do you think, Chips? Up for some hiking in the Berkshire Mountains?"

Chips thought very quickly.

"I like being near the road, Sammy. And besides, I can't climb up mountains with my short legs."

"Okay, Mr. Chips, we'll take the low road! Let's head out to see the covered bridge. I've never seen one . . . we can call this the Grand Detour!" Sam said enthusiastically, and then smiled at Chips.

Chips did not see anything interesting about a covered bridge, nor did he want to walk any further than they absolutely had to, but he knew Sam was determined and he had agreed to no mountain hiking. So, they headed out, soon realizing that signs, like maps, could be very misleading: "Ahead" does *not* mean close by. And now it was the heat of the day. Once they turned down the country road leading to the covered bridge it became harder to stay out of the sun. The woods were far away from the road, so they tried to take cover in the long grasses and fields. Luckily, being low to the ground, they were fairly well hidden. (But if someone had been looking carefully, now and then they would have spied two small backpacks whisking along just above the grasses.)

OVER THE RIVER
AND THROUGH THE WOODS

Finally, the red covered bridge was in view. Sam led the way toward a gently flowing river and they approached the bridge along
the riverbank, drinking some cool water along the way, which
helped with the heat. The river was calm and meandering, and Sam
decided they would stop to rest under the bridge. Looking up, they
could hear an occasional car passing through, the wooden planks
rattling like dull piano keys.

"Chips, this is the life! Free to roam, no rules, no routine. We
can do what we like when we like. How about a catnap?" Sam suggested, smiling at his word choice.

"Okay, but can we take off our backpacks, Sammy? It would
feel so much better," Chips asked (saying nothing about "this is the
life" because he didn't really agree).

"Hmmm, not a good idea. We might need to make a run for it
. . . you never know who's around."

And with this last utterance, the cat who never worried fell
sound asleep.

Sam's words echoed in Chips' mind and, of course, worried
him. However, he was tired from the long walk and it was a very
warm day, and he began to feel sleepy. Being under the bridge was
peaceful and felt safe. Soon he drifted off to sleep.

They had been asleep a short time (a true catnap) when they
were abruptly awakened.

"Excuse me, do I know you?" The voice was loud, somewhat
quacky-sounding, and woke the two travelers instantly.

A large white duck was standing next to them, looking at the
two catnappers with a great deal of curiosity.

"I'm Dolores. *Who are you?*"

It was a question that clearly required an answer. Promptly. Sam
had been startled from a deep sleep, but instantly recovered his
coolness.

"We are . . . Sam Adams and Chips. I'm Sam. Nice to meet you, Dolores."

"Where are you going? I see you're wearing backpacks?" Dolores asked, looking them up and down like a border patrol agent inspecting animals entering Massachusetts.

Chips glanced at Sam. Dolores was obviously used to being in charge. Sam was blinking lazily, not the least bit intimidated.

"The Berkshire Athenaeum. Ever heard of it, Dolores?" Sam replied smoothly.

"Atha what?" answered the duck, shaking her head no.

"Athenaeum. It's an old word . . . from ancient Greece and imperial Rome, named after the goddess Athena . . . in the age of antiquity, it was the name of a school, but now it means library. I lived at the Berkshire Athenaeum when I was young, until . . . well, that's a long story. Anyway, I'm going back to visit, and Chips, here, is coming with me. We're from western Connecticut, near Route 7," replied the well-read, world-weary traveler (now knowing for a fact they were in Massachusetts).

Dolores was obviously impressed with Sam's knowledge and Chips was, too. (Although he was a little confused about what Sam had said.)

"We live at Number Thirteen Rabbit Hill Road. Ever heard of it, Dolores?" Chips asked hopefully, echoing Sam's words.

Dolores turned to look at the small dapple dog, taking a moment to study him.

"I've seen my share of cats and dogs, but I have never seen a dog like you. Looks like someone covered you with paint, without any idea what they were doing. No, I never heard of that road."

Dolores was now shaking her head, and Chips was not sure if what she said was a compliment. Somehow, it didn't sound like it.

"Where is the library?" Dolores asked, turning her attention back to Sam.

"I'll show you on our map," Sam answered, taking off his backpack, pulling out the map, and placing one paw next to the red *X* in Massachusetts.

"We need to get to Pittsfield. Would you know any shortcuts to get there?" Sam asked, realizing this chance encounter with a duck who seemed like the local sheriff might prove helpful.

"Let me think . . . I know a mallard family that lives near Mount Greylock, that's north of Pittsfield as the duck flies. But we can't seem to get our ducks in a row, our social calendars always conflict, so I've never been to Pittsfield. And no reason to go. Sheffield is my home," Dolores answered, in her no-nonsense manner.

Chips decided he liked Dolores. Very plainspoken. He wasn't sure what she meant by getting her ducks in a row, but she understood you weren't supposed to leave home. And she was quite beautiful. Her white feathers were thick and fresh as new snow and her long, yellow beak was sleek and polished looking.

"Well, any suggestions where two gents could find a bunk and a bit of grub?" Sam asked, in his cat-about-town voice (and somewhat reminiscent of Star's manner of speaking).

"I would recommend a campground just over this bridge and up the road, not too far. It's called Rip Van Winkle's RV Campground."

"Who is Rip Van Winkle and what does RV mean?" Chips asked, thinking how great it was a campground was so close—hot dogs and hamburgers for dinner.

"Rip Van Winkle slept for years and years. Obviously, he liked to sleep far too much. My motto is 'early to bed and early to rise makes a duck productive, constructive, and wise.' RV is an abbreviation for Recreational Vehicles, that's camping trailers and vans," Dolores answered authoritatively, looking at Chips like a mother talking to her duckling. Then she turned her gaze back to Sam.

"It's a nice place, good leftovers if you go around after everyone's in bed. But . . . I will also mention, this is widely known to others who are less friendly, you know, the *not-our-kind*. Coyotes, raccoons, rats, they make the rounds at night, too. So, *beware* is all I can say," Dolores said, in a "mark my words" tone of voice.

Chips was impressed by how smart Dolores was. Probably because she got up early every day. However, upon hearing about the late-night campground visitors and the word "beware," he had already decided he did not want to spend the night at Mr. Van Winkle's.

"Well, I wish you good luck and hope you reach your destination, Sam Adams. I have business to do down the river and then I'm meeting my husband, Donald, at Waddle Inn for an early-bird dinner. I would invite you to join us, but you would have to swim to get there," Dolores said matter-of-factly, recognizing the logistical challenge swimming would present (especially to the cat).

As the white duck paddled away, Sam was smiling and shaking his head.

Chips did not think there was anything to smile about, and watching her swim away made him feel sad. He wished Dolores could have stayed longer, maybe overnight; it would feel safer. As she swam out of sight, Chips realized that, so far, everyone they met had been nice.

But the night ahead loomed.

Back at Number Thirteen Rabbit Hill Road, the only word to accurately describe the state of affairs was PANIC. (FRANTIC would also work. So would HYSTERICAL.) Something Sam Adams had thought about, knew would happen, but it had not occurred to Chips. Had it, Sam knew he would be travelling to Massachusetts alone. It would have been all but impossible to persuade Chips to make the Great Escape. And Sam had realized that some kind of explanation needed to be at the ready, just in case Chips thought of this during their travels.

The Lady Next Door had discovered she was two short on the number to be transported to the Vet pretty fast. She asked Bud, first teasing and then quite seriously, where Sam Adams and Mr. Chips were hiding, to please tell her. *Right Now.* But Bud kept his promise and just looked at her blankly (he was good at this) as though he understood nothing and had no worries. She fretted, wrung her hands, and paced the floor after searching the entire house thoroughly (which took time, looking under every bed, in every closet, etc.), only to gasp loudly when she spied the lumber on the floor.

It was then clear what had happened. Of course, the next second she was on the phone with Mrs. S. (they were already at the airport, but had not yet boarded the plane, thankfully) and the nanosecond after that terrible conversation, Mr. and Mrs. S. were flying back to Number Thirteen. (Actually driving, but at times their car appeared to leave the road. Mrs. S. was behind the wheel.)

Police, fire, animal rescue, neighbors, Mr. and Mrs. S. worked two phones calling EVERYONE. Mrs. S. wanted to call the governor and the president—it was close to being a national emergency, maybe a DEFCON two versus one (she had seen that movie). Her voice was bordering on hysteria. Mr. S said no (very gently), it was not the same as a nuclear threat and they would not return the call. Countless times they walked the property, calling two names until they had no voices left. A hundred PETS LOST posters were put up everywhere. (More than you'd ever see for a political election.) The photo for the poster was one of Mrs. S.'s favorites (she had sobbed while making this choice)—Sam Adams and Mr. Chips sitting in front of a blazing fire, wearing their matching Christmas sweaters. (Sam was not cooperative and it took many shots to get a good one, and even then, Mr. S. said he looked like the Grinch.) The local television station came out to Number Thirteen and did an entire segment on the evening news, including what the reporter said had to be filmed as it was found—the lumber on the floor. An inside job if there ever was one, he said (and the only reason the station agreed to cover the story), because obviously, the dog and the cat had decided to escape on their own. A conclusion Mrs. S. was in deep denial about, even after seeing the lumber herself and hearing the reporter's assessment. (And she knew Monkey Business was missing, a fact she did *not* share with the reporter.) Mr. S. did not want her to watch the evening news for this reason, but she did anyway, and it was really awful. She sobbed and said EVERYONE would assume they were TERRIBLE parents—that the reporter made it sound like their own pets had run away from home!! And then she sobbed some more. This continued day after day.

Far away, under a covered bridge in Sheffield, Massachusetts, plans were being made for the evening accommodations. With a lot of talking and reminders of hot dogs, etc., Sam had finally persuaded Chips to go to the campground overnight. The idea they could take shifts sleeping was what tipped Chips to the yes column, although he was very worried about being the one awake when the *not-our-kind* showed up for dinner.

"Let's walk through the covered bridge, Chips. It'll be fun," Sam said, ready to finally move on.

"Someone will see us and then we'll be trapped inside the bridge box . . . no, Sammy, that's a BAD idea," Chips said, shaking his head no.

"Well, then, Mr. Chips, have fun swimming, because we have to cross this river to get to the campground."

Sam began walking up the hill.

"Wait for me, Sammy! Okay, we'll go through the bridge, but only when there are no cars around."

"Yes, I know that, Chips, hurry up."

Sam was the lookout, and he watched patiently until there were no cars in sight. He signaled to Chips when the coast was clear, and then they briskly walked (Sam) and ran (Chips) through the covered bridge.

Over the river and . . . through the woods . . .

To Rip Van Winkle's RV Campground.

RIP VAN WINKLE'S RV CAMPGROUND

Once through the covered bridge the road began to twist and turn and climb. They had not gotten very far when Chips stopped and flung himself down on the grass.

"Sammy, this has to be a mountain. We must be on the Apple Trail," Chips said, now panting, his pink tongue hanging out of his mouth.

"Appalachian."

Sam had stopped, but he was clearly not sympathetic.

"Chips, this is not the hiking trail and it's a hill, not a mountain. Dolores said it was not far after the covered bridge. But we have plenty of time to get there, so we can take a rest if that's what you really need," Sam said, studying him.

"Yes, I do. And . . . can we have our second treat now?" Chips asked hopefully.

Sam seemed to be weighing his response.

"If you want yours, fine. I am waiting, because who knows what we'll find for dinner. Might be slim pickings if the *not-our-kind* get there first."

Which caused a furrowed brow on a dapple head. One, should he eat his second treat now or wait, because what if there was no dinner? And two, the mere mention of the words Dolores had spoken. Chips looked into the woods, wondering who lived there and if they were being watched, and he shivered, even in the heat.

"I guess I'll wait for the treat, but let's rest."

Sam nodded and lay down.

For the first time since they had made their Great Escape, Chips began thinking about Number Thirteen. And Mr. and Mrs. S. And the wonderful aromas of pine-scented candles and pot roast cooking and the soft bed where he slept each night *with them*. And he suddenly felt terribly homesick and afraid for the night ahead, and he wanted to cry. But he didn't want Sam to see him, so he turned away, his eyes filled with tears.

Sensing his sadness, Sam began to talk.

"Did you know Mrs. S. put me in her book? The one about time travel. I have a pretty big part, maybe even one of the biggest and most important. And she told me she was going to use my real name, Samuel Adams, and not some made-up name. Like most authors do."

Chips found himself interested, which was a welcome distraction from his feelings. He blinked his tears away and turned to look at Sam.

"Am I in the book, too?"

"Uh, no. You were not at Number Thirteen when she wrote it." And then, realizing this might make Chips feel bad, Sam quickly added, "So, she couldn't have, but I am sure she would have if you were living there when she was writing."

"Is Bud in the book?"

"Nope. She could only use one cat, and she picked me. I think it was because Bud is not very interesting, and books need to be exciting. I learned that when I lived at the Berkshire Athenaeum. So, he's not in the book either."

Chips thought about this and had to agree. Sam was much more interesting than Bud. This caused him to think of Bud for the first time since they left, which made Chips feel guilty.

"How do you think Bud is doing . . . in prison?" Chips asked.

"Oh, I think he's doing great. Probably their star prisoner. Maybe he has a gold star on his prison cell and they tell all the other prisoners to be like Bud. That would make him feel good," Sam answered, while also thinking it was time to change the subject. He did not want to deal with Chips figuring out Mr. and Mrs. S. were probably now permanently hysterical.

"Hop to, Chips! Onward to the campground, and no stopping until we get there!" Sam said, trying to sound like the cheerful leader.

Chips sighed, stood up, and then trudged along behind Sam, who was skirting the edge of the woods to keep them somewhat camouflaged, his cool green eyes ever vigilant.

The entrance sign had an odd, elf-like man wearing a funny hat and long hair and very long beard, sitting under a tree asleep, next to the words, "Rip Van Winkle's RV Campground." After reading the sign, Sam led the way (rather circuitously) through the campground, avoiding the many campsites, now bustling with activity. Chips had never seen so many people. Most were families with children, who were making a lot of noise. The grown-ups seemed intent on fire building and meal preparations. When Chips observed this, he felt hopeful, aware of how hungry he was getting.

Sam seemed to be on a mission, sizing up each campsite carefully, but for what, Chips didn't know. He did know that not one had been to Sam's satisfaction, because they kept moving deeper into the campground. The campsites were now spread much farther apart, each one well hidden by woods. At last, Sam stopped and whispered to Chips that they would watch for a while to see if this one looked good. Chips settled in close to Sam (he didn't seem to mind), and they hunkered down together underneath a very large fern. And watched.

A small, sleek silver camper trailer was attached to a pick-up truck. They could see a woman inside the camper behind a window and a man outside building a fire in a stone fire pit. In a few minutes, the woman stepped out of the camper door, followed by a medium-sized dog. The dog was short-haired, sandy-colored, muscular, and fit looking. Chips immediately knew he was a yellow lab, because he was identical to The Lady Next Door's dog. Chips had become friends with him when Mr. and Mrs. S. went on Weekend Trips. Sam also knew him. His name was Caramel. Named after the candy, because it was her favorite.

"He looks just like Caramel!" Chips whispered excitedly.

"I know," answered Sam, "and I think it could be helpful, assuming he talks."

A *very* interesting comment. Chips kept forgetting to ask about this, and now he was reminded.

"Sammy, do all animals talk? I've been wondering."

"Most, not all, but most. People can't understand us, but all animals understand each other, as you know from Blueberry Hill and Dolores. It's actually very helpful."

Chips found this amazing. *Really amazing.* And then he thought of Caramel. He did not talk. He was very nice, and he always shared his toys, but he never talked.

"But Caramel never talks, so maybe this dog won't?" Chips asked with some concern.

"We'll find out, later. This is where we'll stay. We can sleep under the trailer for the night."

So, Sam and Chips settled in, waiting patiently for night to fall and the stars to come out at Rip Van Winkle's RV Campground.

During the long wait, they both periodically fell asleep and awoke to grumbling stomachs. It was now dark except for the light of the full moon. There was a soft light inside the trailer. A string of white lights wrapped around an awning that extended out from the side of the trailer, where the couple had eaten what smelled like a delicious dinner (as did the dog). Definitely hamburgers and hot dogs. Sam and Chips had watched the clean-up carefully. The leftovers were all tossed into a nearby garbage can, which was then *covered by a lid.* Chips looked worriedly at Sam, who was obviously thinking hard, so he decided not to ask how a dog with short legs, or a cat, could lift off the lid, get the food inside, and then get back out of the can.

Just as they were pondering this dilemma, the door to the trailer opened, and the dog bounded out—by himself. Sam sprang into action, leaping out of their hiding place and making a beeline for the dog. Chips was shocked. What if the dog was not as friendly as Caramel? As he watched Sam confidently approach the strange dog, even though he was concerned, he felt a surge of pride and admiration. Chips knew there could be no braver cat than Samuel Adams.

"Hello there, the name is Sam, Sam Adams! I've travelled a long distance from western Connecticut, if you know that area, and could use some dinner. Any chance you could help me with the garbage can?"

The lab stopped in his tracks with a look of surprise and curiosity, then his tail wagged once, which Chips knew—*huge relief*—was a very good sign. But he was still feeling anxious—would the dog understand and talk? That question was about to be answered.

"Nice to meet you, Sam Adams. Sure, I can help get the lid off, but you won't be able to get the food out unless I push the can over, and that will make a lot of noise. And then the Mr. will be out here faster than you can imagine. Bears sometimes come around Rip Van Winkle's . . ."

Underneath the fern, Chips froze. Dolores had said—what had she said about the *not-our-kind*?? In his panic, he was not able to remember clearly, but he was sure she had not mentioned bears.

"Hmmm. I see," Sam said, now thinking hard again.

"My suggestion is to wait for the coons. They usually come first and they're very, very good at getting lids off and food out. Maybe they'll share? Look, I should get back inside or it'll raise suspicions, but if you decide to stay overnight, sleep under the trailer. Safer than out in the open. I'll check on you in the morning."

The lab had a kind face, as labs do, and he seemed genuinely concerned.

"Thanks, I'll hang around and see what the night brings," Sam answered confidently.

The dog nodded and headed back to the trailer. Soon all the lights went out, and the only light remaining was from the moon and some red embers in the campfire.

Later that night, Sam told Chips it was time to move from the fern to under the trailer. Chips followed, and soon they were ensconced underneath the trailer, waiting to see who came first to the garbage can. Chips was now shivering continuously. He had never felt more frightened.

The first thing they saw were eyes, many pairs, reflecting like silver orbs in the night. Sam whispered to stay calm and quiet, *no matter what*. Chips was attached like a barnacle to Sam's side. The garbage can was not far from where they were huddled underneath the trailer. The eyes approached in a line, and in the light of the moon they could make out three large raccoons. Chips felt himself relax, a little. Not bears or coyotes, and they even looked *familiar*. (Rocky Raccoon was an immediate favorite when Mrs. S. brought him home, one of two toys he had chosen to go on the Grand Tour.) What happened next was fascinating to watch, and both Sam and Chips were mesmerized. The first coon (the largest of the three) climbed up the side of the can in a flash, pushed

up the edge of the lid with his nose, and flipped the lid onto the ground using one small hand. The lid landed soundlessly in pine needles. Then the raccoon was up and over and inside the can. Moments later, food started flying out of the open top, landing on the ground: leftover hamburgers, hot dogs, buns, tossed salad, gobs of beans, partially eaten corn cobs and watermelon wedges, gooey marshmallows attached to graham crackers, and more. It looked like it was raining food as more kept flying out. The fat coon eventually emerged, climbed back down the can, and joined the others in a feast. Sam whispered to Chips to stay silent and stay put, as the coolest cat (ever) got up and strolled out—to the Feast of the Coons.

"Just sleeping nearby, name is Sam, Sam Adams. Wondering if my travelling companion and I could join you for some dinner? We've been on the road a long time with no food. Of course, only once you are all well satisfied and finished," Sam said casually, yet confidently. If he was nervous, it could not be detected.

Silence. No one answered. Chips was panic-stricken. These raccoons did not talk. But then, there was a voice.

"That would be all right, depending on who your companion is."

It was a deep voice. Chips decided it had to be the leader, and he wondered what raccoons thought about dogs.

"My companion, Mr. Chips, is a dapple dachshund dog. Very small. Very nice. Very polite. May I introduce him?" Sam asked, smoothly.

Chips noticed Sam used "Mr." in the introduction. Very proper.

"Fine. You can both have what we don't eat."

"Most kind, most kind, thank you. Mr. Chips, come and meet our new friends," Sam called out to him.

Chips crept out from underneath the trailer. He was soon only feet away from the three raccoons. In the bright moonlight, he could see their masked faces, white whiskers, bushy ringed tails, and shining, intelligent eyes that looked like silver buttons. They were obviously used to eating very well, and for a moment Chips thought of Buddha Bud.

Then he drew in a deep breath, wanting to sound like Sam.

"Ummm. Nice to meet you, all of you, each of you, sirs. Just wonderful. And, thanks ever, ever so much, for your most generous invitation," Chips said, wanting to impress them with his politeness and manners. (But he could not stop his voice from quaking a little.)

"Pleasure is ours," said the leader, smacking his lips as he dove into another pile of food.

Sam and Chips sat silently, respectfully, watching the Feast. Hoping there would be more than crumbs left.

"So, what brings you to Rip Van Winkle's Campground? If you're going to stay around, we're going to have to make some ground rules. We eat first. Always. No exceptions," the leader said, looking at them seriously, while the other two raccoons nodded in agreement.

"Oh, yes, of course, we would respect that. But we're on our way north, just here for the night," Sam answered.

"Where to?" the leader asked, his eyes shining with curiosity.

"Pittsfield, the Berkshire Athenaeum," Sam answered.

"What's that? Another campground?"

"No, it's where I lived for a while, when I was younger. It's a library, with books, you know?" Sam replied.

"Don't know anything about books. Just food. Do they have good food there?" the leader asked, mildly curious.

He then resumed eating a mostly uneaten corn cob as a person would, holding it with his tiny black hands, chomping in a perfect row and then back again, like a typewriter. Not a kernel was missed.

"Well, it's not a place for food, it's where people read. But they can read about food. There are cookbooks with recipes for delicious treats," Sam answered, smiling, pleased with himself for having found something to say about food and a library.

The leader sat thinking, no longer chomping.

"Do you have any of these so-called delicious treats in your backpacks?"

Sam glanced at Chips. Not expected. At all.

"Nothing that's especially delicious. Just a few cat treats for the road. You know, a quick pick-me-up. We never know when we'll have our next meal," Sam answered, thinking quickly as always.

In a heartbeat, Sam had decided to be honest, just in case. He was confident they would not be interested in cat treats, dining as they did at Rip Van Winkle's All-You-Can-Eat Buffet. Admittance: Mask-Wearing Bandits.

"Sounds interesting. I would like to taste one of these cat treats."

To describe how one cat and one dog were feeling at this moment would be difficult. Suffice it to say, not good.

"Certainly, of course. Let me just get out the small packet, the only food we have, and delighted to share one. Or three, if your friends would also like to sample?" Sam glanced quickly at Chips with a "say nothing" look.

All three raccoons nodded yes.

Sam took off his backpack and pulled out the small bag, opened it and fished out three treats, dropping one in front of each raccoon. The sight was almost funny because the treat was so tiny it could barely be seen. Using their very little hands, which were human-like in their dexterity, they had no trouble picking up the petite treats, sniffing them first, then popping them in their mouths.

Sam and Chips held their breath. It could not be that delicious for the gourmands of the campground. Could not. Except it was.

"That is the most delectable treat I have ever tasted. And you have a bag of them?" asked the leader.

"Well, as I said, it's all poor Mr. Chips and I have to eat, might starve without them. Surely, you would not want us to . . . starve, kind sir?" Sam asked, but he was not too hopeful at this point.

"I'm sure you won't. There are campgrounds and food dumpsters all over these parts. So, if you will give me the bag, we'll leave now, which means you'll have quite a good dinner. Otherwise, we will eat *everything*, and all you'll have for dinner will be your tiny treats."

The leader had spoken. The other two raccoons had stopped eating and were waiting for the response. Three pairs of silver eyes were staring, intently, at Sam.

Chips whispered, "Give him the bag," which, of course, Sam planned to do and did.

They were trundling off into the woods with the cat treat bag firmly gripped in the leader's mouth when an idea suddenly flew into Chips' head.

"Oh, Mr. Raccoon, wait! I want to show you something!"

Sam swiveled, with a *what are you doing* alarmed look in his eyes. Chips whispered to help get his backpack off, which Sam did (for some reason without question), and then Chips pushed his nose into the backpack and out came . . . Rocky.

"Wondering if we could make a trade? You can always find something delicious to eat here, but you won't find this! He looks like you . . . his name is Rocky, and he's one of my favorite toys, but you can have him, he even squeaks! If we can just have the treat bag . . . please, Mr. Raccoon?"

The leader stopped, then slowly turned around. He walked back to take a closer look. The others followed. Soon they were all look-ing at the (kind of beat-up, but still recognizable) raccoon. The leader picked it up, studying it carefully, and squeezed it once (very weak, the squeaker would probably not last much longer, but this would not be disclosed). He seemed to be undecided for a mo-ment. Then he dropped the treat bag, picked up the toy in his mouth, and three lumbering figures disappeared into the night.

Along with them went Rocky Raccoon.

Sam looked at Chips, and for the first time, Chips could see that Sam Adams was *impressed*.

The treat bag once again safely stowed in Sam's backpack, they began to have their Midnight Feast.

Never had anyone (human or animal) slept more soundly than Sam Adams and Mr. Chips under the stars (and under a trailer) at Rip Van Winkle's RV Campground. They had forgotten about tak-ing shifts, and if any of the *not-our-kind* had come along after they fell asleep, they were none the wiser.

Chips slept with Monkey Business safely secured under his chin. Now the one and only favorite.

A LOCAL CELEBRITY

They were awakened early the next morning by the yellow lab. He crawled under the trailer and his face was inches from their own.

"Morning, Sam. Didn't know you had a friend with you . . . ?"

The lab was studying the small dapple face.

Sam and Chips were taking their time to wake up, having slept soundly with full stomachs.

"I can see Old Rip Van Winkle's gotcha under his spell . . . happens to everyone, people and animals. Best sleep is out here under the stars . . ."

Sam yawned and stretched leisurely while looking at the lab.

"Did the coons come through with some dinner?" the lab asked, obviously curious.

"Yes, they did, good suggestion, thank you. And this is Chips," Sam answered in a still sleepy voice.

Chips expected Sam would use "Mr." as he had with the raccoons and was mildly annoyed this was apparently not going to become the standard introduction.

"And . . . what's your name? I don't think you told me?" Sam asked.

"Rockwell. Named after the most famous person who ever lived in these parts . . . Norman Rockwell. I'm sure you've heard of him . . ." the lab replied.

"No, never have. Is he an author?" Sam was thinking there could be no one more famous than Herman Melville from the Berkshires.

"No, illustrator, artist. My owners are artists too, just not famous. We live in Stockbridge, right behind the Main Street. Where are you and Chips headed?"

"Pittsfield. Ever heard of it?" Sam asked, glad to know Norman Rockwell was not an author, so there would be no argument about who was the more famous writer.

"Yep. North of here. A long walk, I would guess," Rockwell replied.

Chips sighed. Loudly. Not more walking.

Sam shot him an exasperated look, as Rockwell appeared to be mulling something over.

"I have an idea. My owners cook breakfast and then go on a hike. When they come back, they set up their easels and paint. They call it Plein Air, means painting outdoors. Anyway, you could hide in the woods until they leave for their hike and I'll save some breakfast for you? Then you could hitch a ride with me in the trailer this afternoon. Stockbridge is north of Sheffield, so it would save you a long trek, unless, of course, you like to hike?"

The lab gave each of them an inquisitive look.

Chips knew he could be best friends with Rockwell. In fact, it felt like he already was. He turned to look at Sam, who was poker faced, so there was no way of knowing what he was thinking.

"Very nice of you, Rockwell. Sounds like an excellent plan. We accept the invitation."

Chips wanted to leap up in the air and do a backflip. He knew he couldn't actually do a backflip, considering the length of his back and his short legs, but it was what he *felt* like doing.

"Happy to be of help. Find somewhere nearby to watch the campsite . . ." Rockwell paused, listening to sounds of people moving around inside the trailer just above them. "Go along now, so they don't see you. I'll save some pancakes and sausage."

Rockwell crawled out from under the trailer. Then Sam and Chips did the same, scurrying into the nearby woods. Rockwell reminded Chips of Buttercup and Beezly. How lucky were they to find someone else who *shared* their food? And notwithstanding the loss of Rocky, Chips was proud about how the previous evening had ended with the raccoons. It was worth the trade. For the first time, he felt like he had done something that impressed Sam.

Just as Rockwell said, his owners had breakfast (the aromas coming from the trailer were mouthwatering) and then left for their hike, telling him, "Guard the campsite and stay nearby!"

Chips was thinking Rockwell did not look like a guard dog.

Once they were out of sight, Rockwell hailed them and they were soon enjoying a delicious breakfast inside a very cozy, comfortable trailer.

Rockwell was studying them as they ate.

"What's in Pittsfield? Didn't you say you're from Connecticut? That's a long way from here."

Sam nodded.

"Yes, it is. But distance doesn't matter when you're going home, to your roots. I'm from Pittsfield. Born there and lived there when I was young, at a library. Called the Berkshire Athenaeum. My name was Melville, after the *very famous* author Herman Melville. *I'm sure you have heard of him.* Long story, but found myself transported to Connecticut . . . which, now that I think of it, I can blame on Rip Van Winkle . . ." Sam smiled wryly to himself and then continued.

"And then I was adopted by Mr. and Mrs. S., very nice people, but it's time to head back to my real home. I'm sure you understand?" Sam said, and then began washing his whiskers.

Rockwell had been listening closely.

"Well, that's an interesting story. Never heard of Herman Melville. So, you're going to stay at the library and not go back to Connecticut?"

Sam arched one eyebrow when Rockwell said he had never heard of Melville. It was hard to believe.

Chips could only think about *the question*, wishing Rockwell had not asked, because he did not want to hear the answer. He wished he had his earmuffs that Mrs. S. put on his ears in the wintertime, because they made everything muffled and quiet.

"I think so. But I'll decide when I get there. If they have another library cat, I won't stay. That I do know," Sam answered.

Chips was astonished to hear this. He had not thought of this possibility, and it gave him some hope. Surely they had a new library cat. *They had to.* Sammy had been gone for years.

"Once we get there, The Library Lady will call Mr. and Mrs. S., their telephone number is on our tags, and they'll drive up and get one—or both—of us." Sam's voice was very matter-of-fact.

"If I was missing, my owners would be very upset. They're probably looking everywhere for you," Rockwell said, looking most serious.

Chips felt his body become perfectly still. This had never occurred to him. Maybe The Lady Next Door had contacted them. He swiveled to look at Sam, his thoughts chaotic.

Sam was, as always, cool. He realized it might come up, that Chips might even think of this possibility himself, and he had thought about the answer.

"They don't know we're missing. The Lady Next Door was going to take us to the Vet after they left for vacation, so she knows. But Mr. and Mrs. S. don't know. They're travelling all over New England for two weeks, and The Lady Next Door doesn't know how to reach them. So, they won't know until they get back. They'll find out we are safe and sound, because we'll get to Pittsfield before they return from vacation, and The Library Lady will have left a phone message for them."

Sam was looking at Rockwell as he answered (very smoothly), and then he turned to look at Chips, calmly and confidently. However, his outward expression did not match his inner thoughts. He knew Mr. and Mrs. S. had to know one dog and one cat were missing, and they had to be going *crazy*. And it did make him feel guilty. The Lady Next Door had their phone numbers and a lot more— Sam had been in The Studio when Mrs. S. gave her neighbor a thick binder labelled "Trip Itinerary." (From the sound of it, the label should have read "Minute-by-Minute Trip Itinerary.") Sam knew The Lady Next Door would have reached them the moment she discovered they were missing.

Chips felt relief flood through him. Of course, Mr. and Mrs. S. didn't know, so they wouldn't be worried. Sam had thought of every detail. Once again, Chips marveled at how smart Sam Adams was.

"Well, that's what I call a well-thought-through plan," Rockwell replied, the admiration in his voice very apparent.

The hikers returned, never knowing there were two hitchhikers underneath their bed, set up their easels and painted for a while, and then closed camp. The silver trailer was soon in motion, heading home to Stockbridge. On the short ride, Rockwell told them that once the trailer came to a stop, they needed to stay under the bed until he barked once, signaling the coast was clear, then make a dash for a large woodpile in the backyard and hide behind it. He told them to wait there while he reconnoitered (whatever that meant) and then he would meet up with them. Smiling mysteriously, he said he was sure they would like Stockbridge. Chips couldn't have felt happier. Rockwell made him feel safe, just like Star. And there was something about his smile . . . Chips felt certain they were going to have a good time. (But he had no idea how good.)

They were waiting behind the woodpile for just a short time when Rockwell reappeared, grinning.

"How about a stroll around Stockbridge? Very nice place. They like cats and dogs. You'll see. Leave your backpacks here, in the woodpile. They would draw too much attention in town. Come on, fellas, follow me!"

The backpacks were quickly dispatched, stuffed between some logs, and Rockwell led the way like the Pied Piper. Sam Adams followed, then Chips, as Rockwell led them across a field and over a stone wall. They quickly arrived on the backside of all the quaint shops and restaurants and one very large white building. Rockwell stopped and turned to them.

"Stockbridge is a place people like to visit. They're called TOURISTS. They go to the Norman Rockwell Museum"—he winked at Sam—"and they like to shop. There are all kinds of shops in Stockbridge, even one for cats and dogs. It's called The Cat's Meow, but they like dogs, too." Rockwell winked at Chips. "You'll see . . . come on, let's get some ice cream first. I'm very well known here . . . my name helps . . . a lot."

ICE CREAM. *Very good words.* Chips couldn't believe it. Rockwell could get them ice cream all by himself, without his owners? Beyond impressive.

Rockwell trotted over to the screen door of The Ice Cream Shop and barked twice.

"Rockwell, I'll be right with you . . . where have you been? Missed you the last few days, buddy. Lots of French Vanilla left!" the man's voice called out from somewhere inside the shop.

Chips and Sam just looked at each other.

Then the man appeared at the back door.

"Well, look at this, you brought some friends, Rockwell! Must be their owners are visiting yours, because they're not locals. Give me a minute, three dishes of French Vanilla coming up!"

Chips was wondering if they could stay with Rockwell a couple of days. There was plenty of time, Sam had said so.

Soon, three bowls were set down with a small frosty scoop in each one, and in a blink of an eye, they were empty.

"Won't need to wash these dishes, no sir! Well, boys, come by with Rockwell anytime. The back door's always open to our favorite canine celebrity!"

Sam was looking at Rockwell with obvious respect (but if one looked closely, also with a trace of jealousy). Chips was wondering what *celebrity* meant, and he was looking at Rockwell as though he were seeing a heavenly vision: a yellow lab with glittery angel wings.

Next they went to the back door of the gift shop—for pets.

Again, two barks, and this time, a woman's voice.

"Right there, Rockwell, honey bear!"

Sam and Chips both looked at "Rockwell, honey bear," then they looked at each other. The name did fit.

"Well, who do we have here? Rockwell, honey bear, you find new friends like no one I know . . . okay, so that's two tennis balls, one large, one small, and one . . . hmmm, mouse, I would say. Be right back, honey bear!" said the pet store lady, as she turned around and walked briskly back into the shop, only to reappear quickly.

"Here you go! Have fun! Bye, Rockwell . . . don't forget, you're my honey bear!"

The pet store lady was smiling at her honey bear, and her honey bear responded by licking her hand. Then he picked up the large tennis ball, followed by Chips, who picked up the small one, and then Sam, who sniffed approvingly and picked up the aromatic mouse.

Rockwell trotted back to the stone wall, followed by Sam and Chips, and dropped his tennis ball between some large rocks— quite visible *and* extractable, Chips observed.

"Stow the toys here, boys, no one will find them. We'll get them on the way home."

Chips looked at Rockwell. The dapple dachshund's expression was crestfallen and doubtful (at the same time). Tennis balls were a special treat at Number Thirteen, mostly because of what happened each time Chips was given one. With a thrill that was not describable, he immediately set to work peeling off the fuzz with his sharp little teeth (leaving a trail of yellow fuzz all over the house). Then, after parading in front of both cats (who could care less) while squeaking the ball as fast as his small jaws could go, he worked tirelessly on getting the squeaker out of the ball. The odd part was, even he did not understand why doing this was so irresistible, because he loved hearing the squeaks (in the brief time preceding demolition), and he actually liked the fuzz on, not off, the ball. Mrs. S. always frowned at him and told him this was *not nice*, it was a NEW TOY, and she would say to Mr. S., "No more tennis balls for Mr. Chips for a long time." (Thankfully, Mr. S. had a short memory for things Mrs. S. said, so it was never a very long time before a new tennis ball would appear.) Every time a pristine fuzzy yellow ball was discovered in the toy basket, it was like having a wild party, followed by some regret for what had apparently happened during the celebration, only remembered when the post-party evidence was inspected. For these reasons, Chips did not want to leave the prize possession, not to mention he was sure some other dog would come along and find it. Most reluctantly, he let the small treasure drop to the ground.

"Do we have to leave our toys here, Rockwell? They might get taken?" Chips asked rather beseechingly, the whites of his eyes showing.

"Yes, we do, and they'll be fine. I've done this for years, no one takes them."

With a deep sigh, Chips picked up the ball and began nudging and pushing hard with his nose, until he finally squeezed the small ball between two rocks, where it dropped out of sight. Chips was very pleased, but Rockwell was shaking his head. He knew it was going to be work to get it out. Sam was watching him with an exasperated look and then dropped his mouse under a nearby bush.

"Sammy, I think someone will find your mouse. You should put it between the rocks like I did," Chips said, looking worried.

"Not worried. Like Rockwell said, no one has stolen his toys for years," Sam replied coolly and somewhat squinty-eyed.

Rockwell was ready to change the subject.

"Okay, fellas, let's take a rest. The best place in town is The Front Porch of The Red Lion Inn. It's an old place, built in 1773.

George Washington slept there, and they never change *anything*, so his room is probably just the way he left it. But it's comfortable, and the tourists like it because nothing ever changes. What they like best is sitting in the rocking chairs, watching other tourists walking by. Never figured out why this is so interesting, but anyway, follow me. People will talk to you and some will want to pet you. Just let them. No one is going to take you anywhere. You're with me."

Rockwell smiled and began walking toward a very big white building.

Now it was Sam's turn to look suspicious and uncomfortable. He tolerated some affection from Mr. and Mrs. S., but that was it. No one else. Chips, on the other hand, had already forgotten about the tennis ball and was looking forward to "taking a rest" on The Front Porch. He *loved* attention, and he missed Mr. and Mrs. S. In a word, he was (quite) chipper, and eagerly followed Rockwell, his flag tail again waving happily, as Sam lagged (or dragged) behind.

They went around to the sidewalk and then up the stairs to The Front Porch. Two lion statues flanked the entrance, and baskets of flowering plants and ferns were hanging from the porch ceiling. Many people were sitting in rocking chairs, passing the time, nothing much on their minds other than dinner. Some were old, some were young. Sam was relieved there were no little children. Children could be annoying to cats. Even babies who were barely walking thought they could pick up a cat. Very bad judgment. Everyone on the porch seemed to take notice when they climbed the steps (ooohs and aaaahs could be heard), and then a young man came out the front doors, wearing black slacks, a red vest over a white long-sleeved shirt, and a black bowtie.

"Well, howdy, Rockwell! Brought some friends today, I see! I'll get you all some ice water. Folks, this lab is a local celebrity, named after our famous local artist. His name is Rockwell. He comes to The Front Porch almost every day about this time. And today he brought some pals. Rockwell's very friendly, you can pet him, but I would suggest just saying hello to the other two. They're not locals," said the man in the red vest, looking at Chips and Sam with a "hope that's okay with you" look.

It was perfectly fine with Sam Adams, but not the dapple dachshund. Whites of the eyes were again on display as he lay flat as a flounder on the porch. He missed (so much) being hugged and kissed by Mrs. S., but he would never, ever admit it to anyone. Most of all to Sam.

Some people strolled over to pet the lab with the famous name. And they murmured hello to the other two; that was all. Chips hoped he would remember to ask Sam what a *celebrity* was. It was the second time he'd heard the word and he knew it meant something important. Maybe he could learn how to be a celebrity when he got back home. It would be amazing to have an endless supply of new tennis balls and free ice cream. As he was thinking these thoughts, the man in the red vest brought out three bowls of ice water. Chips got up and took a drink, as did Rockwell. Sam was obviously not thirsty, nor did he look particularly happy.

A few minutes later something unexpected happened.

"Look, Marvin! Look at this adorable dapple dachshund puppy! I would love to take him home with us!" said an older woman as she kept walking straight for Chips, with a laser beam (or maybe it was a laser gleam) look in her eyes. "He is PRECIOUS, Marvin, just TOO PRECIOUS."

It happened so fast that even Chips could not believe it. Rockwell had blocked her path. She almost fell over him because she had so much forward momentum, and only Marvin's quick reach had prevented the fall. Rockwell did not growl, but his nice face no longer looked so nice. It was rather shocking to Chips that he could look so different. The lady seemed to take notice of his expression.

"Oh my, oh my . . . why, Rockwell, you almost made me fall . . . I just wanted to say hi to the little PRECIOUS. Oh, I can see, he has a tag. Okay, Rockwell, I understand. Little PRECIOUS is already spoken for. Lucky people, must say. Well, we won't bother you . . ." the lady said, looking a little irritated (at Rockwell) and then disappointed (at PRECIOUS).

The lady and Marvin (still holding her elbow) slowly made their way down the steps of The Front Porch.

Luckily, the man in the red vest had gone back inside and had no idea what transpired. And a very good thing it was, because anyone wearing a red vest and bowtie who works at these kinds of places tends to think things like liability and insurance and guest satisfaction are much more important than a local celebrity who hangs out with his friends on The Front Porch.

They had rested for a while (undisturbed) following the departure of Marvin and the would-be Chipsnapper, and then followed Rockwell when he announced it was time to go home. He led them off The Front Porch and around behind the large white building. There was a swimming pool behind the inn and a few people were swimming. Rockwell headed over to a covered area with a long counter where some guests sitting on tall canvas chairs were enjoying afternoon drinks. Above the counter was a sign that said, "Back of the Bank." Rockwell barked once and the man behind the counter (wearing a red vest and black bowtie) leaned over and greeted him.

"Well, if it isn't my favorite barfly, I mean dog! How are ya, Rockwell? New friends, I see . . ."

Next thing they knew, a small plate of cheese and crackers was placed in front of each of them.

"The red lion highly recommends this appetizer. Enjoy, fellas!"

In about one second, Rockwell and Chips could see their reflections in the sparkling clean plates.

"Is there a *real* red lion, Rockwell?" Chips asked, looking around a little warily.

"No, Chips. Just real as in *imagined*. Everyone loves the idea of a RED lion, especially the tourists."

Sam was taking his time licking the cheese spread. It was delicious. Then he studied the name on the sign.

"Do all banks serve appetizers along with cold cash?" Sam asked, mildly curious.

"Nope, only this one, which is not a real bank, because there is no bank in front of the back of the bank, if you get my drift?"

Rockwell grinned at his own tongue twister. Chips was confused (completely). Then the lab nodded for them to follow and he headed back to the stone wall. Chips was soon racing ahead, eager to check on his treasure, which he found immediately by smell. Rockwell came up next to him, sighed, and then got to work. The Stockbridge excursion ended happily when the celebrity's sturdy nose successfully nudged the large rocks just enough for the small dapple nose to reach in and retrieve the perfect tennis ball. Toys secure in their mouths, they returned to Rockwell's house.

The evening plans were about to be shared.

They retrieved their backpacks and headed back to the silver trailer (the trailer door was opened by a large, sandy-colored paw). Once inside, Rockwell invited them to spend the night in the trailer. (The best news to Chips.) And then, in a mysterious tone of voice, he invited them to a *special dinner, fashionably late*, and suggested they take a nap until he woke them up. Not even a second elapsed before Sam thanked him—the invitation was irresistible. Rockwell winked, hopped out of the trailer, and closed the door.

"What's fashionably late, Sammy?" Chips asked, trying to remember the other question he had.

"Probably around nine o'clock. You know, when Mrs. S. puts wine glasses on the table and lights the long candles. Way after we eat."

Chips thought about this. Even after having ice cream and the appetizer at the bank, he could feel the early rumblings of hunger.

"Could we each have two cat treats?" Chips asked, having remembered the recovered treat bag.

"They will spoil your appetite and you already had ice cream and cheese and crackers. That's what Mrs. S. always tells you when you beg for treats before dinner. Since she's not here, I suggest saving them. And remember, Rockwell said this would be a special dinner," Sam answered, in a "case closed" tone of voice.

Chips sighed. Sam was very good at winning arguments. Then he thought of the other question.

"What's a celebrity?"

Sam had a faraway look, as if he was remembering something.

"Someone who is famous. Like I was at the Berkshire Athenaeum. I think I was more famous than Rockwell. I slept in the Melville Room, and no one could go in that room unless The Library Lady was with them. Except me. In fact, I could go anywhere I wanted to, even the Rare Books Collection," Sam answered nostalgically.

"Do you miss being a celebrity?" Chips asked softly.

"Now that you've asked, yes, I do. I do miss it. *Everyone knew my name. They all came to see me.*"

Chips was quiet. His heart ached. Sam would probably not be going back to Number Thirteen.

The trailer became silent and eventually they each curled up and drifted off to sleep (Sam quickly, Chips not).

They did not know "fashionably late" was going to be a long wait.

THE PRIVATE CLUB

W hen they woke up from their naps, Sam was certain Rockwell had forgotten them.

The lab had been fed and was sound asleep, it was the only explanation. There was not going to be any dinner, Sam told Chips, either fashionably late or later than that. Chips was distraught. No dinner??? His stomach was making noises and now it hurt. It is painful when your stomach *knows* there will be no dinner.

There was a nightlight on in the trailer, and above the nightlight was an unusual wall clock. Both Sam and Chips had noticed it when they ate breakfast in the trailer. The clock was in the shape of a cat; the tail swung back and forth, making a slight ticking noise, as the cat's eyes moved from side to side. The clock face was on the cat's belly. For some reason, the clock reminded Chips of Sammy, even though it was a black cat. Staring at it (wishing the cat would say "dinner"), Chips realized the reason was the cat's shifting green eyes—they reminded him of Sam Adams, who was always watching everything.

It was now ten o'clock and they were not sleepy (just hungry), so they watched the clock. What they did not understand was watching a clock is not helpful: time does *not* pass more quickly. Eventually, the cat's eyes and tail going back and forth in opposite directions made Chips feel a little woozy, and he had to look away.

Time ticked away with each swing of the cat's tail.

"Well, Chips, it's now 11:45, almost midnight. We might as well have our treats. Good thing you did not eat your two treats earlier . . . remember to eat very, very slowly . . . all we have until morning."

Sam's resigned voice drifted off as he rummaged around in his backpack for the treat bag.

They were both wondering if Rockwell would remember them in the morning when, suddenly, the trailer door swung open and the yellow lab bounded in, carrying some black ribbon-looking things in his mouth. Rockwell was wearing a black bowtie around his neck, just like the man in the red vest. He dropped the black things and grinned at them.

"Howdy, gents, ready for dinner?" Rockwell asked.

There was a moment when neither spoke. This was so unexpected and so late to be eating dinner. And why was he wearing that bowtie around his neck?

"Yes, of course, we were just talking about it . . ." Sam replied. The relief in his voice might have been noticeable.

"We're headed back to town, but no place you visited today. It's a private supper club, known to very few, just the Members. I was the first Member, so I can always go to the head of the line. And

Members can bring Guests. That would be both of you. You're in for a big surprise—unless, of course, you belong to a private club in Connecticut?" Rockwell asked.

"Ah, no. No, there are no private clubs in Connecticut. At least not near Number Thirteen Rabbit Hill Road. Not a metropolitan area like Pittsfield or Stockbridge. Western Connecticut is . . . boring," replied the cat-about-town.

Chips was absorbing this and feeling worried. Sam thought living at Number Thirteen was *boring*, and he admitted that he missed being a celebrity. It seemed like Rabbit Hill Road was fading away in Sam's mind, no longer where he wanted to be.

"Okay, let's go! The queue opens at midnight, promptly. Oh, here are some black bowties. I keep extras, and they're adjustable. You need to put them on. Private clubs have DRESS CODES for Members and Guests. There are way too many rules to remember, but there's always a reminder of what you're doing wrong in the form of one small German dog. Come to think of it, Chips, you kinda look like him . . . anyway, you'll be meeting him, he's the maître d', majordomo, and all-round major pain in one's derriere. But he belongs to the Founder of the club, so we have to put up with him. Let's shake a leg, boys!"

Grinning, Rockwell lifted one of his rear legs, shook it, and then hopped out of the trailer.

Sam helped Chips with his bowtie and then put on his own, which required some adjustment because his neck was so small. There was a narrow full-length mirror in the trailer and they looked at themselves in the dim light. The bowties were properly placed (one a little droopy) and although it was unspoken, they both liked the effect. Classy. They jumped out the trailer door and Rockwell pushed it closed with his nose, and then they were off, running across a shimmery carpet of dewy grass.

The night was moonlit and star-filled, and Chips was no longer thinking about Sam, because the night felt special. Even magical.

Not to mention dinner was waiting.

As they approached the backside of The Red Lion Inn, they could see a long line of cats and dogs sitting patiently. All sizes, all shapes, all breeds, it looked like the United Nations of Canines and Felines—an utterly incredible sight to Chips and Sam. And it became quickly apparent they were of equal interest to everyone in the queue. Rockwell trotted up to the head of the line, and the otherwise first dog (a handsome Dalmatian) quickly and respectfully began moving back (as did everyone behind him) to the now fourth spot, making room for the three of them. From this head-of-the-line positon, they could now see down a short flight of cement steps to a red door that was partially open. A large round metal lamp attached to the building flooded the stairwell area with light. There was a sign above the door that appeared to be handmade, clearly covering another sign underneath. It read:

Katnip & Bonz
PRIVATE
Memberz Only

At the bottom of the stairwell was a spacious entryway and sitting in it were two dogs. One was a large Husky. He was wearing a baseball cap, sunglasses, and a black leather jacket. *Someone you would only want as a friend*, Chips was thinking. The other dog was sitting on a wooden crate, wearing spectacle-type reading glasses, set low on his exceptionally long nose. He had very short brown legs,

and his long body was mostly black with some symmetrical brown markings. In the light, his black fur looked sleek and shiny, like a seal's. Both dogs were wearing black bowties.

The small black dog cleared his throat and began speaking in a projected voice with great authority.

"Attention! Katnip & Bonz is now open for dinner. Remember to give your name *and* Member number. Proceed down the steps in an orderly fashion, no pushing or shoving. Once we reach the maximum permitted by the Fire Marshal of Stockbridge, that will be it for this evening. Fenway, our Security Officer, will be counting. Now come along."

Rockwell headed down the stairs, followed by Chips and then Sam, and in seconds they were standing in front of both dogs. The Husky dog named Fenway nodded to Rockwell and then proceeded to size up the two non-Members. Chips was wondering why he was wearing sunglasses at night and noticed how muscular he was. His black baseball cap said, "Katnip & Bonz SECURITY." Chips shivered a little. Fenway was intimidating.

Sam's cool green eyes were looking both dogs up and down.

"Rockwell and two Guests."

The black dog stared at the yellow lab, impatiently.

"AND?"

"And that's about it." It was obvious Rockwell did not like this dog very much.

"Your Member number, Rockwell. Why must I always remind you?"

"You know me, you know all the Members, this is a complete waste of time."

"Speaking of time, it's all I have, Rockwell. And with every minute I am delayed, dinner is delayed. I already had my delicious meal, and so did Fenway. We can while away the time, not a problem."

The black dog was now getting the upper hand (or paw), that was clear.

"007. And the name is Bond, James Bond. Not Rockwell," Rockwell said, grinning at the Inspector General.

"Excellent, at least the number is correct. Now, who are *these two?*"

The spectacled face swiveled to Chips and Sam. And if it were possible for one dog to look down his nose at another dog, that would be an accurate description of how he looked at Chips. Not to mention his nose was, in fact, at a slightly higher elevation due to the crate.

"As I said, they are my Guests, Sam Adams and Chips."

"Rockwell, you know there is a limit to the number of Guests you can bring to Katnip & Bonz. In the Bylaws. I believe you have already met your limit of ten for this year."

"You are mistaken. Look it up in that police blotter you keep," Rockwell replied coolly, staring at the clipboard next to the black dog.

The black dog efficiently shuffled the pieces of paper with one very short, chubby paw, getting to R for Rockwell quickly, and then he seemed to need to reread whatever was written—a few times.

"Eight. You have had eight Guests." The black dog did not look up and was still studying the paper, in apparent disbelief.

"Sounds correct to me. And, hmmm, would eight plus two equal ten? Come along, boys."

Rockwell strode into the supper club.

The Guests, however, were delayed with one raised paw by the Security Officer. It was quickly apparent that non-Members were subject to some further scrutiny. Chips was on deck, now sitting directly in front of (and a little under) the long nose.

"Ziggy's the name. Fine Dining's my game. What's yours?"

Chips was at a loss for words and utterly confused. What was he supposed to say? As if reading his mind, Sam whispered, "Mr. Chips is the name, Food Critic is my game." Which Chips repeated, flawlessly (and was very pleased with the "Mr.").

Now it appeared Ziggy was at a loss for words, and before he could find his tongue, Fenway spoke.

"Ya know, Ziggy, this guy Chips kinda looks like you. Wonder if he's a duhshund? That long hair is something else, and look at that paint job!! Maybe his friend here"—he paused, looking at Sam—"had too much katnip one night, found a paintbrush, and went to town when he was asleep!!"

Fenway laughed a deep belly laugh, revealing his teeth. They seemed to glisten in the lamplight. Very white, very long, very sharp. *Definitely should be a friend* was all Chips could think (not that he was possibly being made fun of).

Ziggy was not laughing. (Neither was Sam.) The black dog turned to Fenway with a withering look. *Withering.*

"It is pronounced DOCKSUND. Why is this so hard for you to remember, Fenway?"

Fenway dropped his head. It was now clear who had seniority, and it had nothing to do with body size.

"Interesting occupation, Mr. Chips, I hope you find our food to your satisfaction. You may enter," said the officious gatekeeper, the long black nose summarily gesturing to the doorway, a trace of grudging respect unmistakable.

Chips' tail was a waving flag as he trotted into the supper club.

Next in line was Sam. This was going to be interesting. It was obvious Sam was prepared. He sat facing the black dog, his green eyes gleaming, his tail twitching leisurely, and did not wait for any prompting.

"Samuel Adams is the name, Fame is my game. Named after one of the Founding Fathers. May I enter?"

The black dog once again had his long nose in the police blotter, as though he was looking for the list of Founding Fathers, and then, perhaps finding it, nodded without looking at Sam.

The coolest Founding Father (with the question-mark tail) casually strolled through the door.

Fortunately, the rest of the line moved quickly. Names and Member numbers rolled off the remaining pink tongues (along with, dare it be said, some saliva), all anxious for the fine dining experience to begin. And by some stroke of good luck, no one had to be turned away by Fenway, so there were only happy campers, or Members, "in the house."

A ramp had been placed at one end of a red velvet high-backed couch that wrapped around much of the perimeter of the dining room. In the order they entered, each dog and cat climbed up the ramp and sat on the banquette (although some detoured, hopping onto plush chairs across from the banquette seating, better for conversation, and a few others headed for counter seating). Long tables covered with white tablecloths lined the room. Flickering votive candles and wildflowers in colorful antique glass vases decorated the tabletops, and small crystal bowls filled with ice water and milk were at each place setting. The embossed tin ceiling was painted red, softly lit oil paintings dotted the walls, and a fire was blazing in the fireplace. (The Members enjoyed a fire year round, so the air conditioner was working a bit harder, but comfortable dining is worth any price.) Painted on one wall was a dramatic mural of roaring lions, fiercely staring at one lion who sat by himself, the object of their disdain. Unlike the golden manes of the others, the lion who sat apart was *red*, and he was answering their ferocious roars with his own. Underneath the mural were shelves filled with sparkling crystal glassware and bottles. A long, narrow mahogany countertop with tall chairs ran the length of the mural. Altogether, the room was inviting and snug, with dark-hued colors, burnished mahogany, and dim lighting from brass wall sconces—the fine dining ambience most valued by Members of a private club.

Soon, all were seated and Ziggy once again held court. A little more subdued (or so it seemed), but nonetheless authoritative. He was standing on a wooden crate in the middle of the room.

"Welcome to our Memberz and Guests."

He paused to look directly at Chips (first) and Sam (second). Apparently, they were the only Guests this evening. And apparently, they were important enough to be given some attention, which one can only guess might have something to do with the Food Critic occupation, or being the namesake of a Founding Father, or both.

"Our Guests may be interested to know that Katnip & Bonz was founded a few years ago by my owner, Devyn. With my own pedigree as something of a gourmand, our goal is to consistently meet the exacting standards of our Memberz by offering outstanding service and excellent cuisine. Devyn is the daughter of the *Executive Chef* of The Lion's Den, winner of the *highly coveted* culinary award, 'Berkshire's Best Bistro West of the Serengeti,' for the last five years." Ziggy again paused, looking at Chips with a *take note of that* look, and then continued, "And we are most fortunate that we may use The Lion's Den for our private supper club. And now, ladies and gentlemen, you will hear about the delectable menu for this evening. Please welcome our one and only Chef Devyn!"

Ziggy turned toward the kitchen door, and the look on his face could best be described as rapturous.

All the cats and dogs began to express their appreciation with loud meows (and a few catcalls), happy barking, and paws rapping on the tables. One long wolf-like howl rose above all else, emanating from the excellent vocal cords of none other than Fenway—who was sitting near the kitchen door (having taken off the hat, glasses, and jacket). He got up, and with one powerful paw, pushed open the swinging door with panache. Then he sat at military attention holding the door open with his Super Dog body.

Out from the kitchen strode a young woman, smiling and self-assured. (And very pretty.)

Her ash blonde hair was pinned up, and she was wearing a white shirt with a black bowtie, a long white apron with "Katnip & Bonz" embroidered on the apron bib, and black slacks. It was clear she was a woman in charge of her domain.

"Welcome to all our wonderful Memberz! I'm so glad to see you this evening! Perhaps we are somewhat biased, but Ziggy and I feel that Katnip & Bonz offers one of the best fine dining experiences in the Berkshires, and we very much hope our esteemed Guest, Mr. Chips, agrees!"

She looked over at Chips, grinning. Chips felt the warmth of embarrassment, knowing he was not a bona fide Food Critic. (But he did know the difference between Nutritious and Delicious from living at Number Thirteen, which might be some kind of qualification.) With everyone staring at him, he felt he should do something, so he nodded his head slightly. It was a strange, but also pleasant, sensation seeing everyone looking at him with interest, and he wondered if this was what it felt like to be a celebrity.

"So this evening, our Katnip menu will be: Appetizers of Grilled Frog Legs, family style, and individual crocks of Lobster Bisque, then a Main Course of Wild Salmon sautéed in Katnip Cream Sauce with a side of Oysters and Mussels. And for Dessert, our famous Katnip Mousse for those who walk on the wild side, and Katnip-Laced Decaf Latte for those who are, perhaps, a little less adventurous." She paused, smiling at the euphoric feline faces, and then continued.

"Our Bonz menu will be: Appetizers of Steak Tartare and Ahi Tuna slices, a Main Course of Prime Rib on-the-bone with endless au jus and steamed garden vegetables, and for Dessert, our signature Snowtop Sundae, vanilla ice cream topped with whipped cream and frozen, shaved marrow-of-bonz. And, of course, doggy bags will be provided for the Prime Rib bonz. *Bone* Appétit!"

The menus presented, Devyn took a quick bow, and then winked at Rockwell, who winked back.

It was obvious Chef Devyn *loved* her job as chef.

And emphasizing the Z sound.

There were two reasons for this. *First,* Z was her favorite letter of the alphabet, hence the name Ziggy. (And when they came up with the name of the private club, it was Ziggy's suggestion to change the *S* in Bones and Members to *Z*. It was his favorite letter, too.) *Second*, what none of the Members knew (and probably would not be terribly interested in) was that by day the Chef was a Speech-Language Pathologist, so enunciation was something she thought about—a lot. In the kitchen, she was often heard trilling away, practicing what could best be described as a bouillabaisse of elocution drills and skills. Ziggy did not particularly like listening to all the strange sounds (nor was he fond of the bottom-of-the-ocean soup) and would roll his eyes until she finished. And for some reason he did not understand (at all), she was obsessed with a song called "The Rain in Spain." She sang it in the shower, in the kitchen, anywhere the mood struck her, unfailingly increasing the volume for the refrains, "I think you've got it, by George you've got it!" and "On the plain, on the plain!" and "In Spain, in Spain!" In truth, her voice would not make the leap from kitchen to Broadway, so Ziggy occasionally suffered from mild headaches, but his adoration for the singer more than compensated for any discomfort.

The Chef scanned the room. There was not a single furry face without a smile. Not one. Chips and Sam appeared to be in some kind of reverie, their eyes glazed over, almost hypnotized.

"Before dinner is served, we'll come around with pillows for those who may need a boost to get to their plates more comfortably, and we'll help with the napkins," she said, heading to the nearby pillow bin.

Another young woman appeared from the kitchen and assisted with the pillow distribution and tying a white cloth napkin around the neck of each diner. Devyn went to Rockwell's table first, gently lifting Sam and then Chips as she placed pillows underneath them, tied heavy white dinner napkins around all three furry necks, and then she looked fondly at the yellow lab.

"The regular, 007, shaken not stirred?" she asked with a grin.

Rockwell nodded, and then whispered under his breath, "What I do for England . . ."

Sam and Chips were obviously perplexed.

"It's called an Appletini, made from the juice of fresh watermelon and aged apples, poured into a shaker with ice, and then with a little *shake, rattle, and roll*"—he shimmied in place—"strained and poured. Very refreshing, but something of an acquired taste," Rockwell explained, grinning.

Then Devyn turned to the two Guests.

"I'll bring our signature drinks for you both."

Looking at Chips, she continued, "Popular with hounds is the Wed Wabbit, a delicious concoction of fresh carrot juice, pureed with celery, parsley, and apple, served on shaved ice."

Then she looked at Sam, who was trying not to laugh at the name Wed Wabbit.

"The specialty Katnip beverage this evening is Warm the Cockles, our fall drink that we are previewing tonight. Made from pureed turkey soup, topped with a floater of broth, served warm, of course."

Chips found himself afloat in dreamy drinks, wishing he could have all three. He *adored* watermelon and fresh carrots, and soup of any kind, having had bottom-of-the-bowl samples from Mr. S. when Mrs. S. was not looking.

Devyn smiled and headed back to the kitchen, leaving Sam and Chips speechless.

Soon, the drinks were served in thick pedestal glasses with short, extra-large (and sturdy) straws. They watched Rockwell take a sip, and then they did the same. The Wed Wabbit was delicious. Chips loved drinking from the straw, *very fun*, and was wishing Mrs. S. had these straws. As they enjoyed their drinks, Chips' gaze fell upon some of the Members seated at the long counter in front of the lion mural. Two Miniature Poodles (one white and one chocolate color) wearing sparkly diamond collars and satin bows in their sculpted hairdos were obviously enjoying their private conversations with a Cocker Spaniel and a Cardigan Welsh Corgi, who were sporting black bowties. As Chips watched them sipping their colorful drinks, talking and laughing, he found himself wishing Katnip & Bonz was close to Number Thirteen, for many reasons.

Then dinner was served. It was like magic. The food was perfectly presented, served in warm or cold dishes as appropriate, and the dining room was filled with aromas too delicious to be described. Had a person been out for a late-night stroll and happened to peek through the back door, it certainly would have been a sight. Coon cats, Himalayans, Siamese, and every other stripe and color cat, Collies, Cavachons, Havanese, Hounds, Sheepdogs, and many other breeds were all enjoying the fine dining and good conversation that only a private supper club can offer to the lucky few who have—a Member number.

As they were finishing dessert, Ziggy hopped up on a cushioned chair opposite from Rockwell, Chips, and Sam.

"Thought you might be interested to know we have a VIP Member here tonight. *An Ambassador.* His name is Ambassador Simon Treadway Gato. Right over there," Ziggy said in a lowered, secretive voice while nodding in the direction of a very handsome black and white cat, who was obviously holding court with a captivated audience.

Sam and Chips looked over at the cat. (Sam with interest, Chips less so. He did not know what an Ambassador was.)

"As Rockwell knows, Ambassador Gato greets all the guests staying at The Red Lion Inn. Most prestigious. Very few inns have an Ambassador. Unfortunately, some guests make a huge faux paw," and then he winced, as though the next words would be painful to say, "and they refer to him as a *mascot.*"

With a slight shake of the head, he sniffed dismissively.

"Apparently, they do not keep Emily Post's book, *Etiquette*, on their nightstand."

Sam was certain Ziggy read this book every night before bed. And then the master of rulez continued.

"An Ambassador is *not* a mascot. It is a highly prestigious job and requires a great deal of training in the Diplomatic Corps at the State Department, located *inside the Beltway.*"

This was followed by a knowing look, but neither Sam nor Chips knew what belt he was talking about.

"Top secret clearances, diplomatic pouches and couriers, all highly . . . secretive," Ziggy was now whispering and clearly transported by his own words into a world of intrigue, spies, and secret codes.

After a few moments, he seemed to shake off the spell he had put himself under.

"However, Ambassador Gato never corrects the guests who make this error. Most diplomatic, I would say . . ." Ziggy was now casting admiring glances at the VIP cat. "Everyone wants their photo taken with him, and he is always obliging. I have my own, in a silver frame."

Sam thought, *right next to the Etiquette book on the nightstand.*

"I didn't see him today. We were at The Red Lion Inn with Rockwell, who *is* a local celebrity," Sam said matter-of-factly.

He could not resist commenting, and the implied challenge did not go unnoticed. Black eyes flashed behind the spectacles. But before Ziggy could respond, Rockwell interjected.

"He's an indoor Ambassador, Sam. His duty post is The Lobby. Ambassadors are generally not The Front Porch type. That *precious* real estate is reserved for celebrities," Rockwell explained with a grin, looking at Chips.

Chips was confused (and getting sleepy). Was the cat a celebrity? What was the Diplomatic Corps or the Beltway, and what did Etiquette mean? And the memory of The Front Porch Lady's face was not pleasant. As these thoughts were swirling in his mind, Ziggy apparently decided to change the subject to Mr. Chips, the Food Critic.

"How did we do? Any complaints, Mr. Chips?"

The dapple dachshund was very tired. He had never had such a delicious dinner (or so much food) and it was hard to concentrate. What would a real Food Critic say?? Sam seemed to sense his befuddlement and came to the rescue.

"Mr. Chips has had a busy day. He was at another restaurant earlier today and then busy writing his review. Not to mention this is way past his bedtime." (That comment was not well received, even in Chips' sluggish state. Obviously, a sophisticated Food Critic would have stamina and zeal for his subject, and would *certainly* not have a "bedtime.") Sam continued.

"However, he told me his review of Katnip & Bonz will be five gold stars. Not four and a half, FIVE. And I would have to agree. It is our fervent hope that Rockwell will one day invite us back to your venerable establishment," Sam said, speaking as he did with refinement and elegance, and very good vocabulary for a cat. Something living at a library will do for a person—or a cat.

"You and Mr. Chips will be my Guests anytime you're passing through the Berkshires," replied Rockwell, looking at Sam and then at the black dog. "Providing the Guest Quota has not been met on 007's account according to Police Chief Zigbottoms, or is it Zigmeister?"

Rockwell was clearly enjoying the moment, as Ziggy squinted at him behind the spectacles. These nicknames were his owner's choice, not his, and he did not like to be called either nickname. Embarrassing.

Realizing an explanation might be helpful, Rockwell turned to Chips and Sam.

"Nicknames—all Members have them—some Members call me 'Bond,' but usually it's just plain old Rockwell. Well, BOYZ, let's get home and to bed!" Rockwell declared, hopping down from his seat and heading for the door.

Ziggy was watching the departing Rockwell with a somewhat exasperated expression. Then he looked back at the two Guests.

"If you come this way again, stop by, I'll remember you. I'm good with faces. Katnip & Bonz is open every Friday night at midnight. If Member number 007 is at his legal limit, or out of town, I'll find another Member to sponsor you," Ziggy said, in a tone of voice that was a little friendlier.

Then the spectacled majordomo hopped down and trotted off to find the love of his life in the kitchen. (And to help with the clean-up—the only negative of being related to the Founder—also hoping she was not in the mood for singing.)

A line of Members had formed to exit. The kitchen assistant was taking off their napkins and giving out the doggy bags.

Rockwell carried two doggy bags home in his mouth.

The Food Critic was way too sleepy.

SAMMY'S NEW NAME

M r. Chips, the famous Food Critic, had no memory of going into the silver trailer or what Rockwell told them as he said goodnight. None. Sam, of course, had heard every word, which he reported the next morning.

"Rockwell said he'll come by as soon as his owners leave. They go grocery shopping every Saturday morning. Like clockwork, he said. So, we can go into his house and have breakfast before we head out. Getting closer to our destination each day, remember that, Chips!" Sam smiled at the dapple face.

The dapple face did not smile back. Chips was not anxious to reach their destination, because of what loomed, *the decision*. Yet, he also realized that the sooner they arrived, the sooner he would be reunited with Mr. and Mrs. S. and going home. It was a serious dilemma. Not to mention the night before was probably one of the top five of his whole life, or maybe the top two. Or maybe the best one ever. It would be hard to choose. Luckily, no one was asking him to decide.

"Sammy, I really, really like Rockwell and this trailer and Katnip & Bonz. Maybe we could stay until next Friday night?" Chips voice was noticeably lilting as he asked the question, as in "pleeeeaaase."

"Have to agree, this is very nice, even nicer than Blueberry Hill," Sam replied, looking around the attractive trailer with the most comfortable bed. "But we're on a timetable, a mission, Chips. Timing is too tight. We can't stay another week."

The whites of Chips' eyes showed as he mulled this over.

"What about a few days? Just a few more days? I like Stockbridge."

"No argument, very good place, especially for our kind, as Dolores would say." Sam smiled, hoping the memory of the nice duck would humor Chips. "Maybe we can visit again someday, like Rockwell said. But we must keep moving, and today is clear and sunny, a good day to travel."

"Is it going to be a long walk?" More whites of the eyes.

"Well, I was looking at the map before you woke up. I think we should be able to get to Lenox by nightfall, based on what Star said about maps and scales. Maybe even by the afternoon!" Sam replied brightly. (But the truth was, he did not know, did not have a clue, how long it would take.)

"What's in Lenox?"

"Glad you asked, Chips. We're going to visit a famous author's home! Her name is Edith Wharton, and she wrote a lot of books.

It's a very big house, a mansion really, with beautiful gardens, called The Mount. I read about it at the library."

"Does she know we're coming? Is she nice like Mrs. S.?" Chips asked, hopefully.

It sounded pretty good to Chips. A big house had to have a big kitchen and lots of rooms with soft beds.

"Ah, no. She died a long time ago. But there are caretakers and a lot of people visit, because like I said, she was famous. I heard Mrs. S. say that her great-grandfather was the coachman for Edith Wharton. Mrs. S. has been there before and her brother was married on the property. I know Mrs. S. would like it if we visited."

Chips was thinking all of this over.

"What's a coachman?"

"He took care of the horses and carriages in the stable. A stable has horse stalls like Star's, but Star lives in a barn. A stable is much nicer. Much."

"Why don't we live in a big house with gardens and have a stable with horses?"

"Mrs. S. is not famous, Chips." Sam paused, looking at a troubled face, and quickly added, "Of course, she is famous *to us*, and that's all that matters."

Chips nodded. True. However, this made him think about how much he was missing her and Mr. S. and Bud and Number Thirteen. He had to work hard to push the sadness out of his mind and return to thinking about the day ahead and what would happen.

"What are we going to do there? Are they going to give us dinner?"

"Part of the adventure, Chips, only time will tell. I'm sure it will all work out, though. Look how great this has been so far . . . the Grand Tour just gets better and better . . ." Sam's voice was confident and happy.

Then they both heard the rumble of a truck's engine, the sound fading quickly as the truck pulled out of the driveway. Seconds later, the trailer door opened and there was Rockwell, smiling.

"Come on, boyz, saved you some breakfast!"

They bounded out of the trailer, following Rockwell toward the house. He stopped and turned to them as they approached a screened porch—right in front of something strange looking. On closer inspection, they could see tiny seashells strung together, hanging in rows, making a kind of seashell curtain. It covered the area where one large screened panel would otherwise be.

"Something to tell you guys before we go in. My owners have another pet. A bird. Yellow budgie. Her name is Tweety Bird—after the cartoon character my owner, the lady, is CRAZY about. She wears Tweety Bird slippers and has a Tweety Bird coffee mug and there are Tweety Bird magnets all over the fridge. If I wasn't a local celebrity, I might be jealous," Rockwell said, grinning.

"Anyway, I've been thinking about pulling a little joke on ole Tweety. She's a drama queen and annoying because she talks ALL THE TIME. My other owner, the man, tells her that they're going to adopt a cat named Sylvester. She goes crazy. It's really funny. Then the lady tells her, 'No, Tweety, I will never let him adopt a cat, don't worry your tweet little head'—and it is little, in my opinion. You have no idea how often this is repeated, and the bird believes him each time he says it. So, I want to introduce you, Sam, as the new cat, Sylvester, what d'ya say? I promise it will be worth the performance!" Rockwell asked, with a mischievous gleam in his eye.

Then his expression changed as he thought of something.

"Say, Sam, just a question, you don't, ahhh, happen to fancy a bird for breakfast? My lady owner would die of a broken heart. Just want to make sure . . . ?"

"I do not hunt for my meals, Rockwell. I am what they call a domesticated, and I might add, sophisticated, cat. So, no, I will not eat Tweety," Sam answered, somewhat insulted.

What he did not share was that his one attempt many years ago had ended in utter failure. However, it was survival hunting, which he reasoned would make it different. From that moment, Sam had gained a new appreciation for being fed and not having to obtain his meals as a hunter-gatherer.

"Perfect, let's go," Rockwell said, obviously relieved. "First, you can eat some breakfast in the kitchen. Be very quiet and don't talk so she doesn't know you're here. Her cage is in the living room. She'll call out to me, she *always* does. When you're finished eating I'll introduce you, Sam, as Sylvester. And Chips, you stay in the kitchen, okay?"

"But I want to meet Tweety! Can't I meet her??" Chips asked, feeling quite left out.

"Yep, once she revives from her panic attack," replied Rockwell, grinning.

Rockwell pushed through the shell curtain and they followed. Sam was thinking the pet door made from seashells was very nice, and he was curious about what would happen with the bird. Chips also liked the seashell curtain (and was looking forward to breakfast), but he had mixed feelings about the plan and thought it was a little mean of Rockwell to do this. After all, they were *family*.

Now inside the porch, Rockwell stood up on his hind legs (Chips could not believe how tall he was) and placed his front paws on a lever that extended out from the frame of a glass door. Pushing on the lever while walking a few steps on his hind legs, he slid the door open with ease. Chips was again reminded of the disadvantages of having very short legs. Even Sam could open doors.

Rockwell said, "Shhhh," and then beckoned them to follow. His nails made noise on the tile floor, Sam's footsteps were silent, and Chips crept very slowly, lifting each little paw carefully, so as not to make a sound.

"I hear you, Rockwell, sweetie!!!"

It was a high-pitched girl's voice, a little nasal sounding.

"I missed you, sweetie. You've been gone SO long . . . come here, sweetie!!!"

"It's only been five minutes, Tweety, sweetie!" Rockwell called back, grinning at Sam and Chips.

Sam was trying not to laugh, but couldn't help himself and made a muffled sound like a snicker.

Chips had momentarily forgotten about breakfast. He just wanted to see this bird.

Next to the fridge (that was wallpapered with Tweetys) was Rockwell's humongous food dish. It contained the leftovers: scrambled eggs, pieces of sausage, and chunky beef stew. Sam strolled over to the dish and began eating. Chips' attention then shifted from the bird to the food dish and he sat and waited. Patiently. At last, Sam finished eating (why cats took so long to eat would *never* be understood) and a dapple nose dove into the big bowl. Seconds later, a pink tongue was sweeping the empty bowl over and over again. Although Chips knew there was no food left, it was something he could not seem to stop doing, just like peeling off the tennis ball fuzz and extracting the squeakers.

Rockwell nodded to Sam and headed toward the living room. Sam Adams followed right behind, hidden by the lab's large body.

"Missed you, too, Tweety, sweetie. Parting is such sweet sorrow. But here I am again, to have a word with my favorite bird. And I have a surprise for you, Tweety . . . look who followed me inside, it's your new brother, SYLVESTER!"

Rockwell stepped aside and there was Sam, who proceeded to sit down and coolly study the bird.

She was in a domed brass cage that sat atop a pole much like a floor lamp. Tweety had been sitting in the middle of the perch, swinging back and forth contentedly while awaiting her best friend, when, as they say, the music stopped. She immediately stood up, screeching like she was in her death throes, her body becoming a yellow feathered beach ball, and then she proceeded to fall forward with such speed that she went around and around the perch (many times), holding on with her tiny feet. Finally, the momentum ended and she fell forward, still screeching, straight into the bottom of her cage and out of sight.

"I told you it would be an Academy Award performance," Rockwell said dryly, shaking his head and smiling at Sam.

Chips had been watching from the archway in the kitchen.

"Is Tweety dead??!! Is she okay??!!"

Chips was almost hysterical as he ran into the living room and underneath her cage looking up, but of course, he couldn't see the bird, and there was no sound.

Sam was still sitting down, his tail twitching a bit. He was thinking about Rockwell having quoted Shakespeare and found that interesting, and he couldn't help but find the whole display comical, because it was. Yet, at the same time, he felt a rather strong and uncomfortable twinge. What if the bird had died of shock and then Rockwell would feel terrible forever and so would the lady owner? Just as Sam was pondering the consequences of a good joke gone bad, they all heard her stirring and saying something that was muffled. And then her words could be heard, quite clearly, but she was still out of sight.

"*He has to go, Rockwell,* and you're not my sweetie *anymore. Ever again.* I was here first, the lady told me, even before you, the Stockbridge celebrity dog. How do you think I feel, Rockwell, shut up in this small cage, endlessly waiting for you to come home and tell me about your adventures? I should be out in the world, flying around. That's what birds do. But, no, I am here, held captive like a common criminal. AND I have to listen to the lady talk to me like I am a bird without a brain. You know what they call that, Rockwell? *A bird brain.* VERY INSULTING IF YOU ARE A BIRD. She thinks I'm as stupid as that cartoon bird she is obsessed with. For your information, Rockwell, birds are very smart, some say smarter than dogs. And they should be able to choose their own names. At least you were named after a celebrity. Lucky for you, Rockwell. She could have named you Goofy. She likes that character, too, you know. How would you like to be called Goofy, Rockwell? And how would you feel if you were Tweety Bird and I was you and I told you I brought home someone who might like to eat you for lunch? Or brunch. Or anytime. *How would you feel?"*

Silence, palpable relief (she was definitely not dead), and a kind of communal regret soon settled over the room. Sam and Chips were both impressed. This was no dumb bird. She had made a point. Or two. Sam realized he would go crazy, insane, if he was in her little feet. He glanced over at Rockwell, who was now lying down, with his chin on one paw. Looking remorseful. Sam decided he had to try and save the day.

"Umm, hello, Tweety. I can't see you, but I'm glad to know you're okay. Or at least it sounds like you are. Actually, my name is Samuel Adams, not Sylvester, and I'm just passing through Stockbridge with my friend here, Mr. Chips. Rockwell was nice enough to give us some food and a place to sleep, but we're going to be on our way now. And . . . I am not a hunting cat. By that I mean I would not eat you, ever."

The nasal, high-pitched voice again.

"Well, then, it's nice to make your acquaintance, Samuel Adams. Let me get my feathers arranged and then I'll be able to see you. And your friend, I presume, is not a cat?"

"He's a dog," Sam replied.

Tweety flew up to her perch. She was still fluffed up, but not as much as when she was going around and around. As small as she was, Sam thought she looked almost regal, as her gaze swept the room, settling on one sorry-looking yellow lab. He noticed she had unusually large and expressive blue eyes, which now looked sad and indignant.

"Do you have anything to say for yourself, Rockwell?"

"Yep. Sorry. Bad joke, at your expense. You know it was all in fun, though, right, Tweety?" Rockwell asked, genuinely repentant sounding.

"What is fun for you, Rockwell, might not be fun for me, and you have to think about that in the future."

The bird could be on a debating team. And that team would win. Every time. These were Sam's thoughts, precisely.

"Well, Chips and I have a long way to go, so we will say our good-byes. Let's go, Chips, the open road, or field, awaits!" Sam announced, trying to put a positive spin on things and feeling like it was time to make a quick exit.

"I'll walk you out."

Rockwell had gotten up. His posture looked somewhat slouchy. He seemed to want to slink out of the living room as fast as possible. (And that's what he did.)

"Good-bye, Samuel Adams and Mr. Chips. I'm sorry I won't get to know you better. Have a good trip, wherever you are going . . ."

The now normal-sized yellow bird looked sorry to see them go.

Both Sam and Chips said their good-byes, with Chips reluctant to leave (as always), and he hung back to say a few last words.

"I think Rockwell cares about you, Tweety. He's a very nice dog, he really is."

Silence.

"I know, Mr. Chips. And I'll probably be calling him sweetie again. Maybe tomorrow, we'll see."

Chips felt much better hearing this and trotted through the kitchen and then out through the seashell curtain, which he liked. It was fun to push through it, nose first, and feel the tickle of shells running down his back. Maybe Mrs. S could make a small one for them. He also thought it would be nice to have a bird at Number Thirteen. Just like Tweety. But he wondered about Bud. He liked to eat way too much. Probably not a good idea.

Sam and Rockwell appeared to be having a serious conversation near the trailer. As Chips approached, Rockwell was talking.

"Lenox is a hike. Might be hard to make it on foot in one day. Hop in the trailer while I go check with Zigbottoms. He and his chef live in an attic apartment *above the pet store*. Have to say, when the 'We Have Moved' card was posted at the club with their new address, I was not surprised. That dog is too smart and conniving. Anyway, she sometimes goes to The Mount for catering jobs. Lots of weddings at that place. If she's going there today, I'm sure she'd be happy to take you. So, stay put until I get back. Won't be long."

Sam and Chips hopped into the trailer and waited.

THE AGE OF INNOCENCE
AND
MONKEY BUSINESS

In a matter of minutes, Rockwell was at the base of three flights of stairs on the backside of the pet store building. And in what seemed like three leaps, he was at the top landing looking through an old-fashioned screen door (mostly screen with a thin wood frame).

"Greetings! May one have an audience with His Hineyness, Zigbottoms? 007 here!"

"What do you want, Rockwell? I am occupied. *Very* busy."

The voice came from the back of the apartment. A *very* annoyed tone.

"Just a word. An inquiry, one might say."

Then His Hineyness appeared, trotting down the hallway with the spectacles on his nose, all business. He came to the screen door looking impatient.

"I'm working on the menu for next week, Rockwell. And it's *not* going well. She wants a *theme night*, and the choice is Hawaiian Luau or Throwback '50s. For the Luau, we would ALL have to wear grass skirts, even the guys, and some kind of flower necklace. For the '50s, and I don't even know what '50s she's talking about, the ladies would wear something she calls poodle skirts. I think the ladies who are not poodles would be offended. I told her that and she just laughed. And the guys would wear white T-shirts and dark glasses—kind of like what Fenway always wears. So, I am having a major headache. Major." He paused and seemed to be considering something. "But now that you're here, I suppose you would have an opinion?"

Rockwell smiled through the screen.

"That would be a good guess. The '50s. I am *not* wearing a grass skirt with flowers around my neck. 007 would never be caught dead wearing that. You can tell her what I said, if it will help."

"Hmmm. It might, she likes you, first Member and all. You have some clout, just a little, but don't let it go to your head, which is already big enough," the majordomo said, with a disapproving sniff.

"More room for my very big brain." Big grin.

"Anyway, your Royal Hineyness, I came by today for a reason, not to pass the time of day. Is your better half by chance heading to The Mount today? For one of the big wedding extravaganzas she caters?"

"Why?" Ziggy asked, suspiciously.

He was always protecting her from too many requests, favors, and demands. Already, he had a long Waiting List of Members who wanted to hold wedding receptions at Katnip & Bonz. (They could only be held on Friday nights, and in general the Members did not like giving up their one night at the club for these events. Couldn't she cater receptions at another venue?) And she was constantly juggling speech clients. (One client was coming on Friday nights and she would run him through all the crazy-sounding drills while she sliced and diced whatever—she was very good at multi-tasking.) And just recently, there was some new guy she seemed to like (and vice versa), but anyone of interest was *always* under suspicion. (It took a very long time to pass muster with Zigbottoms.) Thankfully, his opinion held a great deal of clout, and thus far he had dispatched every single one. But for some reason, he thought this one might be a challenge. As he mussed and fussed about all of this, he had not been paying attention.

". . . are you listening to me, Zigmeister? Is she going to The Mount today?"

"Yes, as a matter of fact, she is, for a planning meeting with one of those dippy brides. So, what's your big brain, Rockwell?"

"Can you ask her if she'll take Sam Adams and Mr. Chips along for the ride? In the sidecar—I'm sure they'll fit, you don't take up a lot of room. They're on a road trip, heading north, you know, to check out all the restaurants. Would save them a lot of time to get to Lenox by sidecar."

"Rulez, Rockwell. You don't like them and I do. There are passenger limits for sidecars of motorcycles. It's ONE, and that would be me."

Rockwell looked him in the eye, this time with no sign of patience or humor.

"Look, you really are a royal pain in the bottom—mine, to be exact—with all your *rulez.* And you can't count, we already know that from eight plus two equals TEN Guests. So, ONE sidecar passenger might be three, as in one plus two equals THREE. I agree with Fenway, it is DUHSHUND, as in DUH. You need to lighten up, Ziggy. You would have a lot more fun *and* a lot more friends if you wore a lampshade on your head when you check in Members. And forget the police blotter and Member numbers. Katnip & Bonz is where everybody knows everybody's name—that's what makes it so special. Take my advice, Ziggy, friends matter. So does being nice. Life is too short for rulez all the time. Now, when do you leave for The Mount?"

A long moment. A stare down. One tent folded.

"Two p.m. Don't be late. I'll let her know to expect them. She has some extra goggles."

And with that, the majordomo of "All Things Devyn" turned away from the door and hurried back to his office. So much to do, so little time. But if truth were told, Rockwell's words were replaying in his mind, and would continue to, for quite some time.

As Rockwell galloped home, he felt good. Good about how it ended with His Hineyness and good about helping Sam and Chips, even good that he lived with someone named Tweety Bird. He knew it was going to take time to win her back. What had Ziggy said about time last night—*all he had was time*, that was it. Rockwell knew it was true about living in the country. Things moved slower, time slowed down, and that would help with making reparations with Tweety . . . sweetie.

At two p.m. sharp, they were waiting near the stone wall behind the pet store. Sam and Chips were wearing their backpacks, having checked the trailer for any belongings before leaving, as Rockwell suggested. They had decided to leave the toys; Sam did not seem to want his mouse and the tennis ball was no longer pristine (or squeaky). The only thing they found to be returned to their host were two black bowties. Rockwell told them to keep the bowties as souvenirs of their visit to Katnip & Bonz, and he said, "If one day your travels take you to Stockbridge again, you can wear them at Zigbottoms' fine dining establishment . . ." Rockwell's tone of voice had seemed subdued, but this thought made Chips very happy. And Rockwell had offered Chips his Katnip and Bonz doggy bag, but Sam said Rockwell should keep it, because it might attract unwanted attention from a nose belonging to a *not-our-kind*. (The rightful owner of said doggy bag found this decree very, very hard to accept.)

It wasn't long before the screen door opened and the dashing duo ran down the stairs together, flashes of black silhouettes, one tall and one (very) short. The motorcycle with sidecar, black and gleaming, was parked on the pavement. In seconds, Devyn was lifting Ziggy into the sidecar and then turned to greet them.

"Hi, boyz! Come on over, and I'll put your goggles on and get you strapped in for the ride!"

The Chef of Katnip & Bonz was now dressed in a black leather jacket and pants and wearing a black helmet. As Chips looked at her, sunlight appeared to be dancing around her like a sparkling aura. He wondered how Ziggy was so lucky to have been picked by her. *She was a gourmet chef for dogs and cats and she had a motorcycle with a sidecar.* But instantly, like a pinprick, he felt a strong pang of guilt. Mrs. S. was wonderful, just older, so understandably, there was no motorcycle. And she was focused on Nutritious because she cared about his health. Still, it was hard not to be a *little* green with envy.

Sam and Chips walked over, and she gently fitted them with very small goggles, and then she lifted them into the sidecar, setting them down on a large seat cushion. Ziggy was sitting closest to her, Sam was in the middle, and Chips was on the outside. She had rigged up some kind of seatbelt contraption that allowed her to secure all three with two belts going across their chests. The cushion was thick and perfectly positioned to see the road ahead while sitting down (if you had short legs).

"Okay, we are ready to go! Say good-bye to Rockwell, he'll miss you boyz!"

She grinned at the three of them, and quickly took a photo with her phone. This would go on the Katnip & Bonz Bulletin Board. The Members loved to share their photos with each other, and seeing Mr. Chips, the Food Critic, wearing goggles would give them a good laugh.

Rockwell was sitting down and looked stoic. He knew he would probably never see them again, something Sam also knew, but Chips did not. Youth is ever hopeful and optimistic, which is a very good thing.

The local celebrity raised one big lab paw and waved once.

Devyn started the motorcycle, a loud, powerful rumble, and waved to Rockwell. Then she pulled away, as one cat and one dog looked back at their friend. They both yelled good-bye, but it was drowned out by the motor. Behind *two* pairs of goggles were misty eyes. Sam and Chips both knew Rockwell was . . . special.

As she turned out onto the Main Street of Stockbridge, Devyn drove slowly, as though she understood they would want one last lingering look. They passed by The Ice Cream Shop, The Cat's Meow, The Front Porch of The Red Lion Inn, and a red-canopied *front* entrance leading downstairs to The Lion's Den. Then they were flying, floating along the winding road. The air was heavy, as summer air is, the trees tall and dense, and the lushness of summer's verdant green was everywhere.

Ears flapping in the wind, two hearts still bittersweet, the open road was now calling.

New adventures lay ahead.

Maybe just around the bend.

Before they left Stockbridge, Sam had asked Rockwell privately how this could be arranged—how was it that Ziggy could communicate with his owner what was needed—their ride to The Mount? Rockwell said he didn't know. Everyone knew they had a very close, special relationship, but Ziggy was the only pet who could communicate with his owner Rockwell had ever heard of. Sam knew that most animals could talk amongst themselves, and pets could listen with varying degrees of comprehension to what their owners were saying (cats everything, dogs usually selectively), but that a pet could converse with their owner, well, that was . . . almost unbelievable.

They arrived at The Mount all too quickly.

It had been so exhilarating and interesting that neither Chips nor Sam wanted the ride to end. Sam was thinking it would be the fastest way to get to Pittsfield and thought about asking Devyn. Maybe she could understand all animals? But he decided not to; it just felt uncomfortable.

"Here we are, boyz! Safe and sound! Ziggy tells me I'm a crazy woman driver, but I think he's just teasing me!" She grinned adoringly at her boy.

Devyn parked the motorcycle, turned off the engine, and took off her helmet. Then she took off their goggles and unstrapped them, lifting each one to the ground. With a meaningful look at Sam, she also took off the two backpacks, leaving them in the sidecar.

"Best not to draw attention with the backpacks," she said, smiling. "Okay, boyz, this is the plan. I'm leaving at four o'clock to head to a place called Tanglewood—it's very close by. The Boston Pops Orchestra plays there in the summer. So, meet Ziggy and me back here in about two hours and we'll go together. We can have a *picnic dinner* on the lawn and listen to the music. And I think you'll be able to find a comfortable spot nearby to sleep, as I gather you're on a road trip, heading north. Don't disappoint Ziggy, he wants you to come with us!"

Ziggy appeared to agree, and then they headed off to the mansion for their meeting. (A pair of spectacles had replaced the goggles, which did make him look very serious-minded, for a dog.)

"I want to go to the Tangled Woods, don't you, Sammy?" Chips asked hopefully.

"Tanglewood. Yes, sounds good, at least we'll get some dinner."

Chips nodded happily and then asked, "What are we going to do while they're busy?"

"Wander around, see what we find, tour the gardens, whatever. Look, Chips, right over there is The Stable, where Mrs. S.'s ancestor worked . . . let's go in and look around."

Sam led the way into the large, elegant building where the horses and carriages (and later, motorcars) were kept so many years ago. On this summer afternoon, there were only a few people wandering around and no one was paying any attention to them.

"Star would like to live here," Sam said, admiring the elegant stalls, very large and airy.

"I don't think so, unless he could bring Beezly and Buttercup," Chips said.

"He might want to bring Sapphire, but he wouldn't need the others. He's a stallion and they like to be with other horses."

"They're his friends, Sammy. They eat together every day and talk about all the things going on at Blueberry Hill Farm. And they all like each other."

"Chips, you'll change your mind as you grow older. You will need others less. You'll be more independent."

"But I would never want to be alone or without you or Bud. No matter how old I am . . ."

Chips felt his heart beating faster. This was a serious conversation and it made him nervous.

"You know, Chips, Edith Wharton wrote a book called *The Age of Innocence*. Very important book. Won the Pulitzer Prize for Fiction in 1921. She was the first woman author to win this very prestigious award. Anyway, the title reminds me of you. You, Chips, are living in the age of innocence."

"What does that mean, innocence?"

Sam paused, thinking.

"The short answer is what you love to do, all day, every day— eat, sleep, play."

Sam paused again, still thinking.

"The longer answer is you think things will always turn out well, all happy endings. You think impossible things can come true, like fairy tales. That the friends you have now will be your friends for life. It means you place a lot of importance on things that aren't very important. Like Monkey Business. I didn't need to bring any toys with me, because I am older than you. I have learned that toys are not necessary, at all."

Chips sat down. He tried to blink back the tears, looking away, not wanting Sammy to see. After a few moments, he turned back to look at Sam.

"I want my friends forever . . . like you and Bud . . . but you're really my family, not friends. And I always want my toys. I need them, Sammy . . ." Chips' voice was quaky and very soft.

Sam studied the little dapple face, his expression softened, and then he nodded.

"Maybe you're different, Chips. Maybe you'll be old and even grayer than you are now, and you will still have Monkey Business. Maybe you will always be innocent, and that might be a wonderful thing for you. But not for me, and not for most. Everyone wants to grow up. And as far as us, well, we're kind of a haphazard family. I didn't want to ever leave the library. I loved it there, reading books, looking at all the people, sleeping in nooks and crannies. It was interesting. And it was my home. That's why I'm going back. But no matter what happens, Chips, we'll always have our memories . . . even if we're not together."

Silence settled over them, as did a deep, hurting sadness within Chips' heart. The words seemed to echo in the quiet, airy space: *even if we're not together.* He could not imagine life without Sammy. Tears filled his eyes again, and he was lagging behind as Sam led the way back outside.

"Come on, Mr. Chips. Let's go explore the grounds before it's four o'clock."

Chips noticed the "Mr.," which he had always liked, but Sam rarely used. However, hearing it now made him feel like a cold wind was blowing . . . causing them to drift apart. He did not think about why this was happening. *They were almost at their destination, where a choice would be made.*

CHAPTER ELEVEN

The dapple dachshund followed slowly at first, but soon had to pick up the pace lest he lose sight of the long tail, now moving quickly. They were approaching a vast expanse, and despite his melancholy, Chips was amazed at the vista he was looking at. Sam had also stopped, now understanding that reading about a place could never compare to seeing it with your own eyes. They were looking at a panorama of gardens and fountains, all framed by majestic evergreens.

"Okay, here's some information . . . there are books about Edith Wharton and The Mount at the Berkshire Athenaeum, in addition to the books she wrote. The Mount was built in 1902. Edith Wharton loved gardens and flowers as much as she liked to write."

"So does Mrs. S.," Chips said, thinking flowers must be something all authors liked.

"Yes, she does . . ." Sam paused, remembering the peony and rose gardens at Number Thirteen, and it gave him a fleeting feeling of sadness. "Anyway, Edith Wharton carefully planned all of this—over there is the gravel promenade called Lime Walk because of the border of linden trees, and the walk connects the Italian Garden to the French Flower Garden. There are even Grass Steps cut into a sloping hill in the Rock Garden. Follow me, Mr. Chips, we're going on the Grand Garden Tour! Your short legs are going to have to move!"

Sam was obviously trying to lift his spirits and began to run, with Chips nipping at his tail (in fact, he could have beaten Sam in any race), and it quickly became a game. People turned and stared, but no one tried to stop them. Sam was flying—up and down the Grass Steps, then up to the back terrace of the mansion, then down to the gardens, hopping over flower beds and prancing along the perimeters of large fountains, running back and forth between the linden trees in intricate patterns.

The gardens were so beautiful they appeared to be painted . . . phlox, lilies, hydrangea, delphinium, and dahlias, the favorite flowers of the woman who wrote (often in bed, the handwritten pages floating to the floor like lilies on a pond). Sprawling and magnificent in their naturalness and formality, the gardens were nature's canvas, a looking-glass reflection of the stories penned indoors on a canvas of paper, by a writer who painted with words.

Chips loved running like the wind, following the question-mark tail as it turned on a dime. He realized Sammy was *playing* with him to make him feel better—something he now understood older cats didn't like to do very much, and tears once again flooded his eyes. He *loved* Sammy so much. And as they dashed here and there, he told himself there was still a chance Sammy would choose to go back to Number Thirteen—guaranteed if there was a new library cat. He decided he would start wishing for that *very hard*. It wasn't a fairy tale, so it might come true, and this was just *one* happy ending.

It was all Chips wanted.

They were resting on the grass when they saw the two familiar figures heading back to the motorcycle, and quickly caught up with them. Once secured in the sidecar with goggles on, they were off, and it was not long before they arrived at Tanglewood. As they came to a stop, both Sam and Chips were thinking the same thing—riding in a motorcycle sidecar was *the best ride ever*, and they wondered if it would ever happen again. But their thoughts were soon interrupted as the goggles were removed and the seatbelts undone, and they were lifted out onto the pavement. Then Devyn fished out a wicker basket and a blanket from a compartment in the sidecar, and with a nod to Sam, she put their backpacks in the wicker basket, and they followed her into Tanglewood. There were chairs set up inside a large shed with a roof and open sides, and behind the shed was an expansive grassy area. It looked like a beautiful park.

"We'll go to the lawn, reserved for picnickers with blankets. You probably won't be able to see very well, but we're here to listen to the music and it's perfectly fine for that. We have a lot of time before the concert begins, so I thought we could all take a nap? It was a long night for me last night and for all of you! Okay, boyz?"

Hearing no objection, she found a spot under a pine tree, opened the blanket, and took off her leather jacket and pants, revealing a cotton blouse and shorts. Then they all lay down for a nap. Maybe because of how emotionally exhausted he felt, it was one of the best naps Chips ever had. And when he woke up, he felt much better.

It was now dinner time and many people had arrived with blankets and chairs, and the lawn was filling up. As Devyn opened the wicker basket, it looked like she had brought the Katnip & Bonz private supper club with her (in the basket). Sam and Chips watched in amazement as a white tablecloth was spread over the blanket and then various and sundry items were taken out of the basket. She seemed to know what they were thinking as she unwrapped each delectable package, arranging everything on serving dishes (emblazoned with the name of the private club), and she looked at Sam and Chips, her brown eyes twinkling.

"My real job is working with people who have difficulty speaking. It's called a Speech-Language Pathologist. My other, part-time jobs are Chef at Katnip & Bonz and Caterer for events like weddings at The Mount," she said, pausing to grin, "and being a Caterer means I know how to pack and carry food and set up— *anywhere*—a moveable feast, one could say!"

Again, Chips thought he saw a faint golden aura around her.

Sam whispered to Chips to use his manners and *eat slowly*. Chips nodded, but he was thinking it might be very hard to do, as he gazed at the array of food: chunks of prime rib, grilled frog legs, slabs of salmon, and much more. Devyn poured ice water from a thermos into three crystal bowls, tied white cloth napkins around their necks, set down Katnip & Bonz dinner plates, lit a small votive candle, and served the food to each of the diners. Sam thought this was probably how they picnicked at The Mount years ago and decided even Edith Wharton would have been impressed. (It was obvious the other picnickers sitting nearby were—in fact, enormously so.)

It was twilight as the musicians tuned their instruments and dark when they began playing. The stars were now out, the night air was cooler, and they all enjoyed the music. For Sam and Chips, it was like being back at Number Thirteen, because Mr. and Mrs. S. loved to listen to the Boston Pops, especially in the summer. Of course, this once again inspired waves of nostalgia for one listener, as music often does, but when the orchestra played the rousing *Stars and Stripes Forever*, the evening ended well. They all felt like going on a happy march (each thinking of a different destination).

Then there was another good-bye, and the marching spirit . . . disappeared. Moths flitted under the tall lights that illuminated the lawn well enough to see. Devyn stood up and put on her leather jacket and pants for the ride back to Stockbridge.

"Well, Sam Adams and Mr. Chips, Ziggy and I loved getting to know you both—and remember, Mr. Chips, we're hoping for five gold stars when you finally have time to write your review! Find a place to sleep near the lawn under some thick bushes and you'll be fine. They clean up very well here, so there's no food for any scavengers, which I'm quite sure is known to the locals," she said, grinning at them.

Chips was very relieved to hear this.

"Ziggy and I wish you both safe travels. Come by Katnip & Bonz anytime. As I recall, there are special dispensations in our

Bylaws for Food Critics and their friends, which I'm sure Ziggy will confirm. Such a stickler for rulez, my boy," she said, smiling at her boy. "Oh, and let me assist with getting your backpacks on. Happy to help!"

She got the backpacks securely on and then headed to the motorcycle with the blanket and wicker basket, looking back once to wave. Ziggy hung back.

"Check those rulez, will ya, Ziggy?" Sam asked, smiling. "You never know when we might appear some Friday night at midnight."

Chips' spirits soared at the thought, while Ziggy appeared to be in deep thought.

"I know the Bylaws by heart. There is no exception for Food Critics. But don't tell her. You can come anytime. And . . . you don't need to be accompanied by a Member. I'll tell Fenway," Ziggy said quietly. For the first time, there was warmth in his voice.

Ziggy knew Rockwell would be pleased with this decision. But the majordomo was still smarting (insulted) by the pronunciation of "dachshund," and he was not going to wear a lampshade on his head, *ever*.

"Ciao, boyz. That's Italian. It means good-bye, but hope to see you later," Ziggy said, turning to follow the love of his life.

Two voices spoke softly in unison as they watched him trot away.

"Ciao, Ziggy."

It was late that night. The moon was full and the night had brought much cooler air. Good sleeping weather.

They were sound asleep under a thick flowery bush when Chips was awakened. His chin was resting on top of Monkey Business, and his eyes blinked open, adjusting to the dark. He had heard something, but didn't know what it was. Then he heard it again. Soft footsteps were meeting the forest ground cover, making the faintest crackling sound. A person would not have been awakened, but dogs have excellent hearing. The faint sound was moving farther away and soon the woods were silent again. As Chips peered through the heavily leafed branches, he saw something move onto the lawn under the bright moonlight and then stop. A good distance away from the bush, but now looking back in their direction, *was a wolf.*

Chips' heart was pounding so loudly he feared the wolf would hear it. His thoughts were racing and he was frozen in panic. Then something came over him. It felt like Rockwell was right there, talking to him. He could hear Rockwell's calm voice in his ear. "Quietly, wake Sam. Whisper to him there is a wolf nearby and then run. Run as fast as you can, toward the parking lot. Head left out of the parking lot, that's north. Run as far as you can, don't stop, and don't look back . . . Chips, you are taking the lead this time."

And that was what happened.

Left behind under the bush was one small orange and white striped monkey.

A TERRIBLE NIGHT

It felt like they ran a hundred miles.

Even though Rockwell told Chips not to look back, he did. He had to be sure Sam was behind him. Those few seconds assured him that Sam was following his lead and no one was in visible pursuit. Yet this was small comfort. Chips knew instinctively the wolf could be pursuing them enough to follow but not be seen—the woods were dark and deep and provided a cloak of invisibility. It was why he kept running, until he no longer could. He finally collapsed, not having any idea where they were, knowing he could not run one more step, but also knowing they had gone north following the nearby road. As he had dashed for the parking lot, he thought of turning right, back to Stockbridge, to safety, and then continuing south—to home. But in that split second, he knew he could not do it. Sam would never forgive him. He had to do the right thing, as hard as it was.

North was the only direction they could go.

Chips was now breathing so heavily his mouth was foaming and his lungs were burning. It felt like his heart would burst from the effort. He could hardly breathe, and he wondered if he would die. He couldn't see Sam and tried to call his name, but he had no strength. Chips could only lie where he was, not moving a muscle, trying to get enough air in his lungs. If he did not die from exhaustion, he knew he would be defenseless if the wolf was following, and he whimpered softly in fear.

Then, in the moonlight, he saw him. *Sammy was there, with him.* Relief flooded through his body as his eyes closed. He did not have the strength to keep them open. Everything was fading away, and he felt like he was slipping into an abyss, when water began flowing into his mouth. With great effort, he swallowed.

It was like drinking life.

In his last moments of consciousness, Chips believed he would live.

At the same moment Chips saw the wolf emerge in the moonlight, Mrs. S. awoke suddenly from a restless sleep.

She no longer slept well and neither did Mr. S. They tossed and turned, often getting up, but not speaking, pacing the floor and looking out into the night. From the moment they knew Sam and Chips were gone, life had changed dramatically at Number Thirteen. Mrs. S. could not write, not even one word. She would go to The Studio and try, but soon lie down on a small couch and cry. Mr. S. walked around the yard, but without purpose. It was more like wandering. Aimlessly. He no longer had yogurt for breakfast, and no longer wanted to fix anything or work on projects. Meals were awful. They would pick at their food, but that was it. They noticed Bud had also lost his zest for food, which made Mrs. S. cry even more, because she knew how much he loved food. It was proof that Bud missed them, too. Mrs. S. had spent endless hours looking into Bud's dull eyes, telling him she wished he could talk, that he had to know where they were going and why they left—if only he could PLEASE tell her. Bud realized this was driving her crazy, and he tried to tell her, but his meows just made her cry even more. So, he stopped trying. He knew she would never understand.

At first, Bud had not been too concerned. They were walking (and he knew how tiring that was, even around the house), and it sounded like a long way. He kept expecting The Library Lady would be calling any day, as Sam said she would, once they reached their destination. But as one day passed into the next and The Library Lady did not call, Bud became more despondent and depressed. He began to realize they might not have made it to the library.

And they might never return to Number Thirteen.

This night, when Mrs. S. awoke in the middle of the night, she had gasped loudly in fear and panic. For the first time, she was overwhelmed by a feeling that Sam and Mr. Chips were in terrible danger.

Life at Number Thirteen felt like a nightmare without end.

Chips had fallen into an exhaustive sleep. In his condition, he did not see or understand that Sam had also been physically stressed to his limit. Even Sam did not know how he found the strength to give Chips the water, just that he had to. He had found the water bottle in his backpack, flipped open the spout for drinking, and held it with his paws so that the water would flow into Chips' mouth. When Chips stopped drinking and fell asleep, Sam pushed the water bottle up against a nearby rock and lay under it. There was some water left, and he, too, drank from the bottle of life. Then he looked around one last time. The woods were silent. Nothing moved.

Sam crawled next to the small dapple body and fell into a deep sleep.

COOPED UP

Dawn was breaking the next morning when they were awakened by a loud, familiar sound. Chips thought he was back in the barn at Blueberry Hill Farm, because a rooster was persistently announcing the new day, very close by.

Even before opening his eyes, Chips realized his body was stiff and sore, and he felt exhausted. As his eyes slowly blinked open, he was looking at Sammy's face, right next to his. Chips had never slept this close to him. Sammy's green eyes were open. Calm and serene. Just looking at his face made Chips feel peaceful.

"You did a good job, Chips. You saved our lives," Sam whispered.

The events of the night before were a blur in his mind. It took a while before Chips answered. He was trying to remember.

"I would not have made it without you, Sammy. It felt like I was going to die."

Chips paused for a moment, remembering.

"You gave me the water. But you needed to drink, too."

"You needed it more than me, Chips. You were the leader of our pack last night. I had some after you fell asleep."

"You are my best friend, Sammy."

Sam looked back at the dapple face.

"And you are mine."

Chips felt happiness course through his exhausted body. Best friends did not leave each other.

Then Sam stretched and slowly, with some difficulty, stood up.

"There's a farm close by. We have to get there before the sun is up. Make some new friends, hopefully as nice as Blueberry Hill, who will share their breakfast," Sam said, winking once. "Come on, Chips, rise and shine, up and at 'em."

Sam's voice revealed how tired he was; it was not even close to a bugle call of reveille.

Slowly, Sam managed to put on his backpack and Chips gingerly stood up, feeling his very sore muscles with every move. Amazingly, his own backpack had not moved an inch. By habit, he looked around for Monkey Business.

And then, the most terrible, horrible reality sank in.

"SAMMY!!!! MONKEY BUSINESS IS AT THE TANGLED WOODS!! I LEFT HIM WHEN WE RAN AWAY FROM THE WOLF!! WE HAVE TO GO BACK, RIGHT NOW, SAMMY!!"

Sam sat down and took a (very) deep breath.

"Chips. Calm down and please listen to me, and please don't interrupt. We can't go back. It's much too far. We probably ran a hundred miles last night. That's what it felt like, anyway. And Tanglewood is in the wrong direction. I knew you were going north last night—I saw a sign in the moonlight as we crossed the road.

I have no idea how you chose the right direction, but I'm very glad you did."

Sam paused for a moment, reflectively, and then continued.

"Remember we talked about toys at The Stable, Chips? You have already gotten older on this trip, I can tell. Think about it, Chips. You can survive without him. And you have hundreds of toys at Number Thirteen and soon you'll be back there. And you know Mrs. S.—if Monkey Business is missing, she'll get another one, or two, or three. Not a problem. Okay, Chips?"

"There's *only one* Monkey Business, Sammy. And he's under the bushes at the Tangled Woods. Think about how scared he is right now. I left him. I forgot about him . . . because I was so afraid."

Chips felt like he was going to start crying.

"Yes, you did leave him, Chips. And that was because we were *running for our lives*. He would understand that, believe me. But he is not real, Chips, he's just a toy. He has no feelings."

"He *does* have feelings. I know he does. *We have to go back, Sammy*. I can't go on without him." Tears had filled his eyes, but Chips felt determination surging through his tired body, and it was reflected in his voice.

Sam was quiet, thinking.

"We cannot go back. That's final. There is one reason why we cannot. In fact, it is one word. WOLF. He obviously lives in those woods and we cannot put our lives at risk again."

Chips had not thought of this. The overpowering instinct to get Monkey Business back was all consuming, all that mattered, but he also knew he could never win this argument. It felt like his heart would break right there, into little pieces. Sam was watching him and could see how distraught he was.

"Look, I'm going to think about this, Chips. Maybe there's a way . . . but give me some time and *please* don't keep talking about him, okay? Just know I'll be thinking about how to get Monkey Business back. Is that a deal, Chips?"

"Okay, Sammy." Resigned, but with a sliver of hope (and sometimes when things are very grim, that is all you need to feel like you can keep going).

"Okay, let's go. This time I lead—giving you a break, Chips. But keep up the rear flank, don't fall back . . . keep up with me, Chips." Sam gave him a weak smile.

Chips nodded and Sam led the way.

The sun was rising. They had to hurry.

Where they had stopped the night before was close to the main road, a bearing Chips had been using until he collapsed. He had remembered Sam's plan, to follow the road on the Grand Tour, and that was what he did, while running like the wind.

It wasn't long before they came to the end of a gravel driveway. A very large mailbox (that immediately reminded Chips of Number Thirteen) said "Henny Penny Farm," and a plump butterscotch-colored chicken was painted underneath. Across from the mailbox, on the other side of the driveway, was a farm stand. The shelves were empty, but the hand-painted sign read: "Fresh DESIGNER EGGS." A smaller sign said, "Honor System. $2 Doz. Eggs and $1 Wild Flowers (please return mason jars when flowers die, thank you) No Tax, No Tip."

"What are designer eggs . . .?" Sam seemed to be talking to himself.

"I wonder who Henny Penny is?" asked Chips.

"Oh, she's a chicken in a story called *Chicken Little*. She runs around hysterically telling everyone the sky is falling. They used to read the story at the library to little kids. For some reason, they loved it. I never understood why." Sam did not mention the ending of the story. After their miraculous escape from the wolf, he knew Chips would become completely distraught to find out the chicken had not been as lucky with the clever fox.

Chips was now looking up into the sky. It looked the same as always, now getting brighter blue.

"Chips, it's just a fairy tale, not REAL."

"Do you think there's a crazy chicken on this farm who runs around saying that?" Chips asked, thinking about what Sam had said. "Why else would they use that name?"

Sam studied Chips. A good question.

"Don't know, but we're about to find out. Follow me."

Sam moved quickly up the edge of the driveway with Chips right behind, and soon they could see a farmhouse. No one was around. As they approached the farmhouse, Sam slowed and turned back to Chips.

"See the front porch? There's room underneath. That's where we're going. Stay close, let's go."

They dove under the porch. All quiet. Even the rooster had stopped his racket, having done his job for the day.

"We'll wait here and see what happens," Sam whispered.

"Is it going to be a long wait?"

Sam looked at Chips, rolling his eyes, but before he could respond, someone else was talking. And it wasn't Chips.

An exotic, turquoise blue face with a large beak was looking at them. It almost looked like there was a crown on its head; small decorative feathers rose vertically from the back of the head in a fan shape.

"I saw you running up the driveway and thought I would greet you. Welcome to Henny Penny Farm. We, that is, the peacocks who live here, all wanted 'Peacock Paradise,' but we were outvoted. Easy to do, since there are twice as many of *them* as us."

Sam and Chips were speechless. They had never seen a peacock before. The voice was surprisingly deep. The creature looked so beautiful they both assumed it was a girl.

"My name is Sir Lancelot. Named after one of the Knights of the Round Table." The peacock paused and then added as explanation, "Knights wore very good-looking armor. So, what are your names?"

Oddly, Sam did not immediately respond, so Chips answered. He already liked Sir Lancelot.

"Mine is Chips. Actually, it's Mr. Chips, but you can call me Chips. And this is Sam, Sam Adams. He goes by Sam to everyone, but I call him Sammy. Sir Lancelot, are there crazy chickens here who think the sky is falling?"

The peacock laughed.

"There are a few chickens I think are crazy, but I'm sure they would not agree. However, to my knowledge, none think the sky is falling. Where are you two from?"

Sam had now recovered and answered.

"Western Connecticut, near Route 7. Ever heard of it?"

"No, but we don't get out much. Is it far from here?"

"Yes, a good distance. We've been travelling for some time. Wondering if there might be something to eat?" Sam asked, hopefully.

The elegant face nodded.

"Follow me, quickly. You'll have to get into the chicken coop before the farmer comes out with breakfast, which will be anytime now. Hurry!"

The blue face disappeared and they scurried out, following what they could not see from underneath the porch—a very long tail, or train, made of gorgeous, shimmery feathers. The peacock was now moving quickly and they had to trot along to keep up. There was a small building in the distance, and as they got closer, the peacock slowed and then stopped. Ahead was a sturdy fence made with heavy wire and wooden posts that went all the way around the building, including a large grassy area.

"Wait just a moment, and I'll open the fence door."

To their complete amazement, Sir Lancelot took a running start (that looked a little awkward and not particularly aerodynamic) and then, as if by magic, he lifted off into the air, flying above the coop, making a large circle, his long tail feathers sweeping behind him like a royal cape.

"I can't believe it . . . maybe pigs can fly," Sam whispered under his breath. (He had heard Mr. S. say this whenever he thought something was impossible. Mrs. S. would say something like "Maybe we'll win the lottery today, I have such a good feeling about it." And Mr. S. would say, "That'll happen when pigs fly.")

Chips was utterly transfixed; it was the most unbelievable sight. He did not even know a peacock was a *bird*, and he certainly would never have guessed such a bizarre-looking creature could fly.

Sir Lancelot seemed to be enjoying his flight and swooped around gracefully for another few minutes before landing inside the fenced area. Then he went to the fence gate, wiggled something with his beak, and the gate opened. He called for them to come. Sam and Chips moved slowly toward the gate, almost like they were under a spell.

"Follow behind me. I have to introduce you first, and then they'll decide if you can go into *their* coop."

Sir Lancelot walked toward the coop, and soon they could read a handwritten sign on the door. It said, "CHIX ONLY. PRIVET. NOK FRST (EXEPT FARMR)." Then, to their complete aston-

CHIX
ONLY
PRIVET
NOK FRST
(EXEPT FARMR)

ishment, his sweeping tail became a huge fan, which completely concealed them.

"Good morning, henny pennies! We have some travelers who would appreciate a respite in your cozy coop, and perhaps some breakfast, if you would be so generous to this wayfaring twosome," Sir Lancelot said in a lilting, ingratiating tone of voice.

"Who, who's there?" asked a suspicious-sounding voice coming from a small round hole cut into the coop door at ground level on the left corner. This was followed by a few low, nervous warning clucks.

"Oh, Susanna, please don't cluck at me! It's your friend Sir Lancelot, may we enter, please?"

The peacock sang the familiar melody, but with new lyrics. Neither Sam nor Chips could believe it. Sir Lancelot was a flying troubadour. His serenade, however, was met with silence behind the coop door, so he continued (speaking, not singing).

"Susanna, and ladies of the coop, our guests are a small, friendly dog named *Mr.* Chips and a nice cat—very nice—named Sam Adams. They're just passing through . . ."

Then ensued what can only be described as chicken chatter. It was squawky and noisy and everyone was obviously talking at once. Chips was trying to hear if any crazy-sounding voice was saying the sky was falling, but it was too garbled to make anything out. He was thinking about Sir Lancelot singing, and how funny that was, when the coop quieted down.

A different chicken's voice began speaking authoritatively, through the round hole in the coop door.

"We have to look at them, through the peephole, so close your fan tail and move aside, Lancelot, and I'll take a gander."

Lancelot complied, seemingly used to the bossiness.

"Hmmm. Come closer." An order.

Sam and Chips moved closer to the door and sat. (If they had been wearing hats, they would have been holding them in their paws.)

"Look okay to me. You take a look, Mrs. Hunt-n-Peck."

"I-I th-th-think the-the-they look fine, Mrs. Cluck," said Mrs. Hunt-n-Peck.

"All right, they can come in. But just for breakfast and then they move along. We can't have hangers-on staying in the coop, it's already crowded."

It was clear Mrs. Cluck ruled the roost, so to speak.

The door opened slowly from the inside. About a dozen chickens, all strikingly different, were staring at the two visitors. Some were on the floor; some were perched on shelves or rafters. There were square wooden boxes on one shelf, and a few chickens were nesting in the boxes. The scent of the hay wafted out the door, reminding Chips of Blueberry Hill Farm. Breathing in the natural fragrance made him feel more relaxed, and he decided any place with hay was a good place.

"Mr. Farmer will be here any moment with breakfast. Might not be to your liking, but it is to ours. He can't see you inside the coop, so I suggest getting yourselves underneath the hay on the lower shelves and waiting until he comes and goes. And don't make a sound," said Mrs. Cluck in a drill sergeant's voice.

"I'll be around the farmyard. Holler if you need me, Mrs. Cluck. Expect to see you before you go, Sam Adams and Mr. Chips," Sir Lancelot said, and then departed in what might be described as a regal way, nodding to everyone, then slowly turning with his cape of feathers cascading behind.

Sam and Chips never answered Sir Lancelot. They had (somewhat tentatively) walked up the short ramp leading into the coop and were too busy getting well hidden under the hay. Mrs. Cluck (a golden yellow chicken) inspected their efforts, shaking her head and clucking with some dissatisfaction. Using her beak, she began moving some hay around for better camouflage and adding more hay on top of the backpacks, which had been poking through as plain as day. Just as she was making the final adjustments, Susanna (a black and white chicken) called out from her position at the peephole that Mr. Farmer was on his way.

"All quiet! Stay put, Sam Adams and Mr. Chips. Don't make a peep."

Another order from Mrs. Cluck. The pecking order was crystal clear.

The coop door opened and through the hay, they could see Mr. Farmer pretty well. He was older, wearing faded denim overalls and big black boots, and carrying a large metal bucket.

"Feedin' time, gals! Good food for my brood, yep, layin' pellets, Edna's fresh cow's milk from MacGregor's Dairy Farm, and a bit o' ground-up oyster shells, that'll do ya. Protein, calcium, flax seeds and minerals, just what the doctor ordered. Keep up your good work, gals, we'll have some more customers today . . . at least before lunch," the farmer said, as he scratched his chin a little, thinking.

"Bad summer storm comin' in around noon. You'll have to batten down the hatches, no time to fly the coop!!" the farmer said, chuckling quietly. "So let's have a look and see if you gals have been busy—any designer eggs ready to go?"

Then the farmer walked over to where Chips was hiding. One of the chickens was sitting near where he was hidden. The farmer's big hand was feeling around for eggs right next to Chips, and almost touched him, when Mrs. Cluck began clucking. Loudly. Followed by Mrs. Hunt-n-Peck.

The distraction worked. The farmer immediately headed over to them, happy to find many eggs in the nesting boxes where they were perched. He oohed and aahed over the water-colored eggs, praising his "prize layers," and then carefully filled his soft hat with eggs. He set the hat down in the hay, poured the gritty pellet mixture from the bucket into a large feed trough, and then filled something that looked like an upside-down water cooler with fresh water from a nearby hose. As he picked up the hat and closed the coop door, he reminded them to stay inside and hunkered down.

"C-c-close c-c-call!" exclaimed Mrs. Hunt-n-Peck.

"Yes, that it was," answered Mrs. Cluck. "And now we hear there's a summer storm brewing. Well, Sam Adams and Mr. Chips, looks like you'll be staying awhile. Fine with us, no one likes being out in a storm. Once it clears, you can be on your way. Now, come out of your hiding places and see if you like breakfast for chickens."

Both Sam and Chips had pushed their heads through the hay, knowing the coast was clear. Listening to Mrs. Cluck, Chips was reminded of Dolores. Mrs. Cluck was orderly and disciplined, and underneath her butterscotch feathers, he could tell she was nice, just like Dolores.

Having heard the description of breakfast, however, both Sam and Chips were glad they would not be staying long—this was nothing like Buttercup's or Beezly's meals (not to mention private club cuisine). The chickens bellied up around the trough, making soft, happy clucking noises as they ate. They obviously enjoyed eating and seemed to eat a lot. Sam and Chips glanced at each other. Even though it was not appetizing, it was food, and they hoped something would be left. As the last chicken sauntered away, quite stuffed, Mrs. Cluck nodded to the two visitors, who gingerly approached the trough. There was some food left, and they began eating. Looking at each other, they didn't have to talk. The food was gritty with no taste at all. Chips had never eaten so slowly. But it was far better than no breakfast, and they thanked their hosts with the same appreciation as if it were the fine dining experience of Katnip & Bonz.

Then they settled in for a long day, cooped up, as it were, with their new feathered friends.

As the morning wore on, introductions were made, and like the Chicken Judge at a County Fair, Mrs. Cluck proudly provided background information on each bird. (So much information that it became hard to remember everything and who was who, at least for Chips.) She said their names had been chosen by the farmer's wife, and even though their feathers were different colors, they were a flock, *a family. And that birds of a feather stick together and take care of each other.* Chips glanced at Sam, who had no expression. Chips hoped he was listening.

Susanna was introduced as a Plymouth Rock chicken (also called a Barred Rock, the Chicken Judge said), because her black and white feathers looked like a geological rock striation. Mrs. Cluck said her full name was Susanna Winslow, named after one of the few women who came across on the *Mayflower*, an experience that would have given anyone a case of the nerves. And it was obvious Susanna-the-chicken was the nervous type. Hence her post at the peephole, always wanting to see who was coming to the coop.

Then Mrs. Cluck introduced herself as a Buff Orpington, of English heritage (specifically from Kent, but she had no trace of an English accent) and said she preferred not to talk about herself, but did admit to being a bit "broody" in the summer months. Chips wondered what "broody" meant. Mrs. Cluck was a big chicken with gorgeous, thick golden yellow feathers.

Mrs. Hunt-n-Peck was introduced next. She was an Easter Egger, whose eggs were the most beautiful and prized of all. (Mrs. Cluck reported this with pride and without an ounce of jealousy.) She went on to say that Mrs. Hunt-n-Peck was a friendly, smart bird and cold and heat hardy—laying eggs all year round. She said this pleased Mr. Farmer because most of the chickens, except for herself and Mrs. Hunt-n-Peck, did not lay eggs in the winter. Mrs. Hunt-n-Peck's unusually large eggs came in all the colors of a rainbow: blue, green, rose, sage, olive green, cream, like an Easter surprise, Mrs. Cluck said, clucking approvingly. Mrs. Hunt-n-Peck was clearly embarrassed by all the compliments and had tucked her head into the hay. Mrs. Cluck did not mention her odd way of speaking, and Chips wondered why it was hard for her to talk.

Then the other chickens were introduced by their names, an assortment of Marans (notably with feathered feet and chocolate-brown egg layers), Araucanas, Ameraucanas, and Cream Legbars (all strictly blue egg layers), one Barnevelder (native to Holland with glossy feathers and laying light brown speckled eggs), and last but not least, Mrs. Cluck introduced an "ornery" Silver

Spangled Hamburg chicken, native to Germany. The Hamburg chicken was exceptionally attractive (with markings like a Dalmatian), and she obviously knew it. Mrs. Cluck said Frau Hamburg needed room to roam, that she was a free-ranger, and to please forgive her attitude, as she did not like being cooped up, at all. Then she said Frau Hamburg's eggs were glossy white, nice enough but (sad clucks) *unfortunately* not the same color as her gorgeous black and white feathers. If looks could kill—that was how Frau Hamburg looked at Mrs. Cluck. Chips thought she looked like one mean chicken and knew he would keep his distance.

Then all eyes were on the two visitors. It was obviously their turn. The dapple dachshund's head was swimming with all the unusual names and who laid what color eggs. Fortunately, Sam was their spokesperson and took the microphone (so to speak) from Mrs. Cluck. A good speaker with an excellent vocabulary, in no time he had neatly summed up their journey, where they were headed, and why. There was silence when he finished, until Mrs. Hunt-n-Peck asked *the* question.

"Are you g-g-going t-t-to st-st-stay at the li-li-librrrr-ary?"

"Not sure. If there's another library cat, definitely not. If not, I don't know," Sam answered.

Chips felt the familiar sadness ripple through him, like a skipping stone on a calm lake. Both Mrs. Cluck and Mrs. Hunt-n-Peck looked at him with concern; it was clear they were both motherly chickens. He found himself again wondering why Mrs. Hunt-n-Peck spoke so strangely, as though she had a hard time getting the words out, and he thought about Devyn. *She could help Mrs. Hunt-n-Peck.* But how would she ever find Henny Penny Farm? The thought was perplexing, and as he was trying to think of what could be done, he dozed off, still very tired.

Midday he awoke.

The wind had picked up and was rattling through the eaves, and as the first big drops of rain fell loudly on the tin roof, there was knocking at the coop door. The official peephole watcher, Susanna Winslow, announced it was Sir Lancelot "with his contingent."

Hearing this, Mrs. Cluck clucked to herself, muttering about overcrowding, and then she sighed.

"Let them in."

Susanna pulled the door open with a small rope attached to the bottom of the door, and in they came. SIX peacocks. But as Chips looked at them, he noticed some looked different from Lancelot, quite plain in comparison, with no fancy tail feathers. Three had a long train of feathers and three did not.

"Most gracious, Mrs. Cluck. We appreciate the shelter. I don't know why Mr. Farmer doesn't build us a peacock coop."

"Lancelot, dahling, it should be a Peacock Palace, not a coop. We are royalty."

One of the plain peacocks was looking affectionately at Lancelot. He seemed a bit embarrassed.

"Guinevere, my love, the chickens have been most kind to allow us to share their lovely coop. And it is charming—homey, comfortable. Lovely fragrance, hay. I would say it makes a home."

"I agree, Sir Lancelot! Sammy and I stayed at Blueberry Hill Farm and they had hay, too," Chips interjected brightly, forgetting he had not been introduced to the other peacocks.

All the other peacocks turned to look at who had spoken. They were quite startled and appeared to be upset.

"Oh, I forgot to tell you about our visitors. They arrived early this morning. The dog is Mr. Chips and the cat is Sam Adams . . . where are you, Sam?" Lancelot asked, looking around the coop.

"Up here."

Sam was now on the highest shelf, just beneath the rafters. His habit of checking out places from the highest story had not diminished. Second-Story Sam was at his post.

"Oh yes, there's Sam Adams! Easier to get to high places if you had wings, Sam!" Sir Lancelot exclaimed.

"I suppose that would be true. But I like being a cat."

"Glad to hear it. Not much we can do about our fur or feathers!" Sir Lancelot said, chuckling at his own quip.

"Lancelot, you and the others can settle here, in the middle of the coop. This is going to be a long afternoon. Let's make the best of it," Mrs. Cluck said, on duty as always.

The peacocks sat down, a ring of brilliant blues and greens that seemed to shimmer with tiny sparkles, the long feathered trains looking like an exotic carpet with jeweled eyes.

There was one small window near the eaves through which a black, angry sky could be seen. The wind had picked up. Ventilation came from two long, narrow screened openings that ran along under the rafters on the backside of the coop. The air coming in smelled like a freshwater lake and swept through the coop, cooling everyone down. Heavy rain began to fall and there was an occasional thunderclap. Inside the coop there were softer noises, some clucking, some whispering amongst the peacocks, but altogether, a quietness, even a peacefulness, settled in as the animals waited for the storm to pass. Chips knew he was safe, as was Sam, and he was grateful they were not outdoors. He felt happy to be in Mrs. Cluck's coop with the chickens and the peacocks. For the first time since leaving Number Thirteen, Chips thought about chewing on a bone. It was something he did often at home, because that's what dogs do when they are happy and content. Sam saw him trying to get his backpack off and jumped down to help him, and soon he was chewing contentedly—very glad he had been allowed to pack one bone. And Sam spread out Mrs. S.'s scarf on the hay. It *almost* felt like home.

After a while he had his fill of chewing, and breathing in the faint smell of her perfume, he fell into another deep sleep. He was still very tired from the night before.

Chips slept a long time, most of the afternoon. There were crosspieces of lumber in the eaves, and some of the chickens roosted there. All the coop residents napped or dozed much of the afternoon. When Chips awoke, the storm had passed, but now it was getting dark as night approached. He finally felt rested and much better, but then his stomach twisted. He remembered what Mrs. Cluck said—they had to leave once the storm ended. Leaving the safety of the coop at night was something he could not even imagine doing. He glanced up at Sam, who was looking at him. It was strange, but true, that in the time they had been together on the Grand Tour, Chips felt he could sometimes read Sammy's mind. And at this moment, he knew they were thinking the same thing.

Suddenly, there was scratching at the coop door. It was light and weak, but everyone heard it. Susanna went to the peephole and looked out.

"It's the rabbits who live near the garden."

"This is not Noah's Ark. Dear me, the storm has passed. Well, let them in. They must have a reason for coming, they keep to themselves most of the time," said Mrs. Cluck with another big sigh.

The door was pulled open and in hopped two big white rabbits with long ears and four baby rabbits. Chips immediately thought of the mailbox at Number Thirteen. The big rabbits looked just like the painted one.

"Thanks so much, Mrs. Cluck. We have come to warn you and in hopes we can stay the night. Tragic news from the MacDonald

Farm just up the road. Heard it from the coons. I'm very sorry to tell you they lost some of their chickens last night . . ."

"What do you mean, lost? Did they run away or did someone take them?" Mrs. Cluck asked urgently. She knew the family, mostly Welsummers and Penedesencas, excellent layers and very nice birds.

The large white rabbit hung his head. His soft long ears hung down and touched the floor.

"No. They were . . . killed. It was a wolf, they think."

Fear and panic swept around the small coop invisibly, but the visible reactions were immediate. Loud gasps, horror-stricken faces, and for two of the coop residents, shock, followed by a slow, horrifying awareness of how easily it might have been them. In fact, should have been them.

"It cannot be a wolf, Mr. Rabbit. I know that is little comfort, and does not take away the fear of whatever it was, perhaps a black bear or a coyote. But it was not a wolf. The last gray wolf was seen in the Berkshires long ago. There has not been another sighting or evidence of a wolf for years. I know this because I've heard it from Mr. Farmer many times. He talks to us thinking we don't understand, but of course, we do. And he's told us, 'Don't worry, gals, no wolves here in the Berkshires.'"

Mrs. Cluck hoped this would help to calm everyone down and looked around the coop. Not a lot, apparently. But it was about to get much worse.

"There is a wolf. We saw him last night. At Tanglewood."

Sam's factual voice came from high above. Words cannot draw blood, but they can inflict pain, and these words drew cries of shock and disbelief.

"Why did you not tell us this before, Sam Adams? Were you going to leave and never tell us, putting all of us in extreme danger for not knowing?"

Mrs. Cluck was staring up at Sam, her voice filled with anger and contempt. All the others were rallying around her, looking up suspiciously at the cat whose words struck fear in their hearts.

Chips felt desperate. He had not even thought about telling the chickens. He assumed the wolf had not followed them and stayed near the Tangled Woods. He didn't know how Sam could explain this, and why had he said anything at all??

"I thought about telling you as soon as we arrived, but then I decided not to. One, because of the panic it would have caused, and two, because we escaped, and at one point we were only a short distance from him. We ran for a long time and stopped when we could no longer run. He could have found us and killed us both. Easily. So, I didn't think any of us would be in danger this far away. However, Mrs. Cluck, I already decided I was going to tell you, *privately*. And I was going to ask if we could spend the night tonight and leave when the sun was up. But if you prefer we leave now, we will."

Chips could not believe Sammy's last words. How could they leave the coop at night with the wolf close by? The silence was deafening. Everyone waited for the judge and jury, Mrs. Cluck, to speak.

But it was not she who spoke.

"I-I, th-th-think S-S-Sam and Mr.-Mr. Chips have d-d-done nothing wrong. They sh-sh-should stay in th-th-the coop."

Mrs. Hunt-n-Peck had spoken. Mrs. Cluck never did, and it was over with a nod from her to Sam.

They would stay the night, everyone would, all together.

Later that night, as Chips tried to settle in, he thought about Monkey Business for the first time since arriving at Henny Penny Farm. He really, really wanted to sleep with him this night. And the thought of his most favorite toy all alone under the bushes at the Tangled Woods made him want to cry. His heart felt heavy, and he was very afraid.

Monkey Business and Mr. and Mrs. S. were far, far away.

And the long night was ahead.

It was the middle of the night. One dim light bulb was on inside the coop.

They were all restless and sleeping lightly, so when the distant howl rose to meet the full moon, they all heard it. Everyone awoke and froze. They all looked at the coop door. Before going to bed, Sam had directed the peacocks to use their bodies to push on a small burlap sack labelled "Layers Pellets" that was propped up near the door. It had fallen over, but only covered the hinged side of the door by a few inches, so it offered little protection. If the wolf pushed on the side of the door that opened, Sam knew he would probably get in. He had not slept at all, realizing how vulnerable they were. Everyone else seemed to think the door was now secure and had dozed off. But Sam had remained awake, trying to think of a way to secure the door.

In two silent leaps, Sam was prowling the coop, now desperate for anything that could reinforce the door. Then he spied an old piece of lumber, leaning up against the wall in the right front corner of the coop. The cool green eyes scanned the walls. Two wooden brackets—they blended in with the wood walls—were on either side of the coop door. *Just like the pet door at Number Thirteen.* The only problem was, of course, how to move an unwieldy and heavy piece of lumber.

CHAPTER THIRTEEN

Let it be said that in moments of crisis, having a team is much better than being alone. And in those moments, as has been proven innumerable times, adrenaline can work in mysterious ways.

Sam instructed the peacocks to push on the lumber with their bodies, gently, with the hope it would fall along the wall and rest on the first bracket. Sir Lancelot understood the plan and took the lead position, coaching the others to nudge the lumber *carefully*, while applying pressure to keep it against the wall. Three peacocks were on one side to try to keep the lumber against the wall as it came down, while the three on the other side pushed. As everyone else held their collective breath, miraculously, the piece of lumber slid against the wall and came to rest (on an angle) in the first bracket. Just as they were about to attempt the very difficult second phase of trying to move the lumber into both brackets, they all heard it again. This time the howl was closer, but it was impossible to tell how close.

Later, Chips could not remember thinking he should do this; he had just done it, instinctively, when he heard the second howl. He jumped down from where he was on the second shelf and hopped up next to the rabbit family who were huddled together on the first shelf. Chips whispered something to the parents, who nodded with tears and fear in their eyes, and with great gentleness, he picked up the first baby bunny by the back of its neck. Then he jumped to the second shelf (even with short legs, dachshunds are surprisingly good jumpers, better than rabbits), set the baby rabbit down, and went back for the others, one at a time. Using his nose, he covered them with hay, and then he lay down (very carefully) on top of them.

They all heard the sound of digging coming from somewhere behind the coop. The wolf was digging under the fence. It would only be a few minutes before he was at the coop door.

Sam studied the angle of the lumber leaning in the bracket. The lumber extended across the opening of the coop door by just a few inches. It might be enough to secure them, but Sam wanted the lumber in both brackets if at all possible. He whispered urgently to Sir Lancelot, who nodded his understanding. Sam ran up the angled lumber like an experienced gymnast on a balance beam to the end, hanging on with his claws. He knew his weight alone would not be enough to lower the lumber, but thought it might help if the lumber could be positioned properly, like a stone on a seesaw. It would be up to Lancelot to do the rest. With an incredible stroke of luck, there was a stack of pellet sacks along the wall underneath the lumber about four feet tall. The right height, with a peacock standing on the pile, to move the lumber from its current angle to horizontal. However, only one peacock could fit underneath the lumber while crouched on the feed sacks. Alone, Sir Lancelot would have to attempt to lift the lumber so that it would be nearly level with the brackets, while simultaneously pushing so that it would reach the second bracket. The brute strength of a giant prehistoric bird named Hercules (not Sir Lancelot), human-like (not avian) coordination, and tremendous good luck, combined, might not be enough to succeed. They were lacking two out of three, and the luck part, well, that could never be counted on.

Then the wolf was at the door. He growled, a guttural, fierce sound. Sam looked at Chips. Their eyes locked onto each other. The green eyes held him. And in that moment, Chips was not afraid.

Instantaneously, as if by some magical force, the lumber moved and then slid down smoothly into the other bracket, with Sam riding on the end, like a seesaw coming to a stop. Sir Lancelot collapsed on top of the feed sacks.

Not a sound was heard from anyone inside the coop.

However, they were not the only ones who had heard the wolf's howls. Mr. Farmer had heard and he had loaded his shotgun. It seemed like only seconds later when they all heard the single shot. Blistering, echoing, right near the coop.

It was not until the next morning the farmer knew something miraculous had happened inside the Henny Penny Chicken Coop.

The night the wolf had been knocking at their door.

LAST LAP

They all slept the sleep of the brave who are triumphant. The sleep of those who have faced possible death and survived. It is the deepest sleep of all. And only the rooster's persistent crowing finally roused them. From a small open window at the top of the barn, the rooster was heralding the new day, at the top of his lungs.

Mrs. Cluck began to stir, as did the other chickens. Then the peacocks awoke, as did the rabbits. Chips was awakened by the tickling sensation of little bodies moving underneath him. As he slowly opened his eyes, he knew this was a morning he would never forget. Sam was watching him from his high perch near the eaves. Chips realized that he had been able to face death because of the green eyes he was now looking at. They had locked onto his own, never wavering, strong and brave.

The coop began to hum softly with the sounds of life, and Mrs. Cluck was quickly getting her managerial feathers back into place. Soon, she stood up and cleared her throat.

"Good morning, everyone. It is not possible to thank Sam Adams and Sir Lancelot enough. They saved our lives last night. I know I speak for everyone when I say that we are forever indebted to you both," Mrs. Cluck said, obviously emotional, and she took a moment to regain her composure.

With transparent gratitude, everyone looked up at Sam and then at Sir Lancelot (who appeared to be recovering, much helped by Guinevere's adoring looks at her knight in shining armor).

"Mr. Farmer will be arriving soon with breakfast, but there's no rush for Sam Adams and Mr. Chips to hide, because . . . Mr. Farmer is going to have a hard time getting into the coop today."

There was silence. No one had thought about this dilemma (except for Mrs. Cluck and Sam, both of whom were clearheaded, even under stressful circumstances). All eyes settled on the well secured (as in a fortress) coop door.

And no one, not even Sam Adams, had any idea how to get the lumber out of the brackets.

So, they waited. It was not long before Susanna Winslow spied the farmer coming toward the coop, feed bucket in hand. He was whistling, but stopped as soon as he pushed on the door. Then again, harder. The door that always opened into the coop with the slightest pressure did not budge. Puzzled, he set the bucket down and began assessing the situation, recalling the events of the night before.

The farmer knew they were all right because he had been up from the time of the second howl, watching from a second-floor window facing the coop. He saw what appeared to be a large coyote approaching the coop from the back of the pen. It was moving quickly, staying close to the side of the coop, but he did not have a good shot. In seconds, the animal was at the coop door, growling. He had held back for a moment before pulling the trigger, because he did not want to shoot directly into the coop if it could be avoided. The animal was in the shadow of the building, but he clearly did not jump or push on the door. Then, suddenly, the animal had turned away, retracing its steps and heading toward the back fence. It was at that moment the farmer had taken his shot. He saw the animal fall and he knew the chickens were safe, so he had gone back to bed. Awake before the rooster crowed, he went to the coop yard immediately, and that was when he made the shocking discovery.

The coyote was, in fact, a young, muscular gray wolf.

And he knew that no wolves had been seen in the Berkshires since 1860.

The farmer's thoughts returned to the current predicament. He realized the door was barricaded from the inside. But how was that possible? Then he remembered. There were brackets on either side of the coop door; he had seen them years ago when he bought the farm and fixed up the coop, perplexed as to why they would be on the *inside* of the coop. Yet, how could some chickens have made a fortified barricade? It was a complete mystery. He went to get a ladder from the barn, put it up against the side of the coop, climbed up, and looked down through the window.

Looking back at him were six peacocks, a dozen chickens, and a family of white rabbits. He shook his head in amazement. Then he saw the piece of lumber across the coop door. He whistled long and low. This was—what was it? Peacocks, chickens, and rabbits had managed to put a heavy piece of lumber into two brackets to protect themselves? It was some kind of miracle. He very slowly made his way back down the ladder, went inside, and called the wildlife authorities and then the *Berkshire Eagle* newspaper. This was definitely newsworthy.

All the coop residents (except for a well-hidden dog and cat) were overnight celebrities. The newspaper photographer had climbed the ladder and taken the prize photo through the window, proof positive of what the farmer had described on the phone. Then the farmer was interviewed, and once out of the coop, all the animals were photographed for the front page article. (All except for two.) The headline was going to read: "MIRACLE AT HEN-NY PENNY FARM."

The part about getting the animals out of the coop was not without its own drama. The Fire Department had come, which no one in the coop understood, because there was no fire. The firemen proceeded to cut an opening in the side of the coop—noisy and stressful for those cooped up—and then one fireman crawled through. Carrying an axe. If you are a chicken, this is NOT a welcome sight, so there was a lot of flustered squawking amongst the soon-to-be celebrities. And when the coop door was finally opened, they all dashed out—to escape the dreaded axe, and once assured of safety, to bask in the lights of their newfound stardom.

The local wildlife authorities confirmed what the farmer knew. Wild Eastern gray wolves had last been seen in the Berkshires over a hundred and fifty years ago, and the nearest known population was in Canada. Which meant this gray wolf had come alone from Canada, crossing the St. Lawrence River, then down through Maine, negotiating hundreds of miles of roads, bridges, and communities to get to the Berkshires. And they were certain the wolf had come alone. This was also unusual, because wolves normally travelled in packs. Shaking his head, one of the wildlife experts said to Mr. Farmer, "How this wolf managed to make this trek will never be known, but one thing is—the myth of the Lone Wolf has been proven to be *true.*"

Around noon things began to return to normal at Henny Penny Farm.

Mr. Farmer had covered the opening in the side of the coop with a piece of plywood. The rabbits had hopped happily away (the parents profusely thanking Chips), the chickens (especially Frau Hamburg, who was zooming around) were at last roaming free inside the large fenced pen, and the peacocks were grazing here and there (Sir Lancelot resting, Guinevere waiting on him hand and foot), all while one dog and one cat were still lying low, stomachs growling. (The feed bucket had never been emptied into the trough, and the feathered residents had never missed it. Who can think about food if you are a newly minted celebrity?) It was not easy, and certainly not fun, to have to remain under the hay while all the excitement was going on right under their noses. Chips wanted to participate very badly—the magical and much coveted word "celebrity" was being tossed around, and Sam was wondering if they would all be going to Hollywood by private jet. He had read about celebrities and private jets at the library (in the Magazine Section, which The Library Lady did not seem to approve of for some reason). But as Sam knew, they could not risk being discovered, and he whispered to Chips to hang in there. Had anyone been listening (but no one was paying any attention), there were deep sighs coming from one small pile of hay.

It was late in the afternoon when Mrs. Hunt-n-Peck happened to overhear several important conversations. First, she overheard Mr. Farmer telling his wife that he needed to take one of his tractors into Pittsfield for repair. Then she heard him call the repair shop and arrange to bring it in the next afternoon. And then she heard his wife tell her husband to remember to take her library books back because the repair shop was close to—*the library*. Mrs. Hunt-n-Peck reported what she heard that evening when all the chickens were back inside the coop. It was hard for her to get it all out, but with patience and perseverance, she communicated everything, and to Sam's ears, her words were perfect. But to a pair of dapple ears they were *very* hard to hear.

This would be their last ride, the last lap.

Samuel Adams, formerly known as Melville, was going home.

THE BERKSHIRE ATHENAEUM

Mr. Farmer brought the chickens a special dinner late in the afternoon, once all the commotion ended and the celebrities could finally rest. Normally, they ate their one meal in the morning (foraging the rest of the day), but this was a celebration, and Mr. Farmer felt he should do something special. And special it was. The feed bucket was heaped with scraps of steak, cooked vegetables, warm corn chowder, pieces of blueberry muffins, gravy and mashed potatoes, and more. After pouring it into the trough and telling them how proud he was of his girls, Mr. Farmer left the coop whistling a happy tune. Mrs. Cluck invited the peacocks to join them, and they all came, walking regally into the coop. Happily, Sir Lancelot seemed to have recovered quite well from his exertions of the previous night.

Once Mr. Farmer left the coop, Sam and Chips emerged from the hay, both looking forward to a delicious meal. Surprisingly, the chickens were not impressed (muttering and clucking, saying it was not as good as their usual fare, which seemed hard to believe). Nor were the peacocks, with Guinevere pronouncing it would be so much more delicious if some bugs, grasshoppers, and crickets had been mixed in. Which meant one cat and one dog could eat their fill, and they did.

As night fell, Chips was full and once again feeling content to be in the coop. He liked the chickens and the camaraderie, and he realized if push came to shove, he *could* live in a barn. Or even a coop. But at this moment, all he could think about was wishing time would stop. To stay with his new friends a while longer, and more importantly, to delay what was coming.

The final destination.

The next day dawned early, as usual. Roosters are nothing if not punctual.

Chips hadn't slept well and wasn't hungry. He ate just a little of the pasty, tasteless food and noticed Sam hardly ate either.

Time passes very slowly when you are waiting.

The day dragged. Mrs. Hunt-n-Peck was on alert all afternoon for the trailer that would haul the tractor, to flag them on quickly so they could get under a large blue tarp at the far end (very good news when Sam heard this). He had worried about where they would hide in an open trailer, realizing if there was no place to hide they would have to go on foot. And he knew Chips was not up for any more walking.

The signal came late in the afternoon.

Their backpacks were on and they had said their good-byes. Again. Chips did not like this part of the Grand Tour. Each time he met new friends he was so sad to say good-bye. But this time, because of what they had been through together, it seemed hardest of all. His eyes were filled with tears and he could see that Mrs. Cluck and Sir Lancelot were also emotional. They had been together in a life-or-death situation, an experience none of them would ever forget. Even the cool green eyes appeared to be sad and thoughtful as Sam said his farewell.

Upon hearing the signal cluck, Sir Lancelot pulled open the fence door to the pen, and Sam and Chips darted out, heading for the trailer while the farmer was in the barn getting ready to move the tractor. All the peacocks and chickens gathered to watch from behind the wire fence as the two small figures ran up the ramp into the trailer and dove under the blue tarp, out of sight. Not seen was a family of white rabbits, hanging back near a stone wall, solemnly watching the departure of two heroes.

The tractor secured and the trailer gate closed, the farmer started the truck, heading to Pittsfield under threatening skies. With two additional passengers, along for the ride.

The rain began to fall as they made their way down the long gravel driveway of Henny Penny Farm.

Underneath the blue tarp, Sam and Chips were not talking. They were listening to the raindrops noisily hitting the plastic, each thinking their own thoughts. Sam was feeling a nervous excitement as he thought about where they were now headed. But there was something else. He realized he also felt uneasy . . . there were many unknowns. The library had been his home when he was young, and he wondered if it would look the same and if the same Library Lady would be there—hoping she would, because she would know him. If not, he knew he might not be recognized by anyone. And he wondered if there was another library cat, and what he would decide to do if no other cat had replaced him. For the first time, Sam realized the homecoming might not be as easy as it seemed when the Grand Tour was planned.

Chips was feeling as blue as the color of the tarp and as bedraggled as the wet weather. He thought the dark skies and rain were appropriate for this day. A day he wished would never come. Looking at Sam, who was obviously lost in thought, Chips wished he could read his mind and know what his decision would be— he would rather know right now than go through any more agony of not *knowing*. But unlike at other times during their journey, he could not read Sam's mind. They were inches apart, but they might as well have been separated by a million miles.

He closed his tear-filled eyes.

Soon they were aware of traffic noises, horns, other vehicles nearby, and a lot of starting and stopping. They both knew they were getting close, and before long, the truck pulled into a parking lot and stopped. The engine was turned off, then the trailer gate was opened, and they could hear men's voices as the tractor was being backed out. Sam was watching from underneath the tarp, and as soon as the tractor was off the ramp and no one was in sight near the back of the trailer, Sam told Chips to follow him. They were two streaks, and if anyone saw them, no one yelled out.

Sam headed for some nearby bushes to get his bearings.

Looking out from underneath the branches, Chips could see they were in a town like Stockbridge, only much bigger and noisier. There were many buildings, a lot of traffic and noise, and people walking on sidewalks carrying umbrellas; it did not feel like a safe place to be on their own. Sam was moving around the bushes to see if he recognized any landmarks when he saw the familiar brick building. Mrs. Hunt-n-Peck had heard correctly—the tractor repair shop was close to the library.

"We're very close, Mr. Chips! I can see it. The Berkshire Athenaeum is right over there. Let's wait until there are fewer people around, though."

Chips nodded. *Mr. Chips.*

The rain started to fall harder, and they were getting wet, even with the bushes offering some protection. Chips was thinking about the nice raincoat Mrs. S. had bought for him, and how she told him he was too adorable when he was wearing it (a handsome Burberry plaid), telling him he could be on the cover of *Hounds About Town,* her favorite magazine (she had told him so). Then he was thinking about Mr. and Mrs. S. and Bud and Number Thirteen, and realized he would be back home soon, and that thought made him feel good, until the black cloud named Sammy returned. And then he thought about Monkey Business. Chips had not bothered Sam as requested, so he couldn't mind *one* question.

"Sammy, what about Monkey Business? Just wondering if you've thought of a plan . . . to get him back?" Chips asked, rather timidly.

Silence.

"I haven't had time to think through the logistics, quite complicated, as I am sure you realize."

"What is logistics?"

"How to do something, the plan. How we, or you, get back to Tanglewood."

Or you.

Silence.

"Well, maybe we can call Devyn. She could take us to the Tangled Woods . . . or me."

Chips whispered the last two words; they seemed to catch in his throat.

"Don't know how we would do that. She didn't give us her telephone number and even if she had, not exactly easy for either of us to ring her up."

Sam glanced at Chips with a wry smile.

"Say, Mr. Chips, it's getting stormy and late. We need to try and get inside before the library closes. Tally-ho, follow me."

Mr. Chips, again.

Sam was obviously changing the subject, and Chips realized it was not a rosy outlook, getting Monkey Business back. This made his heart even heavier, and he decided the stormy weather was perfect for the current state *of everything*. Sam was moving fast, Chips followed right behind, and soon they were hiding in another hedge, right next to the library building. With the heavy rain, people were huddled under hooded raincoats and umbrellas, so they had not been seen as they ran toward the library.

"I'll go on a bit of a tour, get my bearings, check out the perimeter. As Rockwell would say, I will reconnoiter with you soon. Stay right here until I return, okay?"

Chips nodded once, the whites of his eyes very noticeable, and Sam left.

Sam skirted the building, all of it becoming more familiar as his memory stirred, remembering. Some of the large windows went almost to the ground, so he could look in easily. The lights were still on, but it didn't look like there were many people inside. He knew the library closed at a certain time, so it could be any time now. He also could not see the Main Desk where The Library Lady always was, because that would require going to the front entrance and he didn't want to attract attention, at least not yet.

He moved to the next low window and stopped, in his tracks. Sitting alone at a table near the window was someone he recognized. *He remembered this person.* The boy had been in high school then and came to the library to study. He liked the library cat and would always talk to him. Sam remembered hopping up on his open books and papers and lying down, looking at him. The boy would laugh and ask how he was supposed to study. And the library cat would just stare back as if saying, "Let me stay, I don't want to move." Usually the boy would let him stay for a while, jostling his papers a bit to get the one he needed, or moving him to another open book. He was always very gentle and he smiled a lot. What was his name?? It started with a *B* . . . *then he remembered . . . Brenton.* In that moment of remembering, he instinctively cried out and stood up, putting his front paws on the window. Rain had soaked his fur and the window was covered with raindrops. The young man heard the cries and turned away from his laptop, looking at the window. He stared for a moment and then slowly got up and went to the window and knelt down. Studying the small, wet face, he began shaking his head and grinning, and then he shouted, "MELVILLE!!!" Then, "IT'S MELVILLE!! HE HAS COME HOME!!"

Home. He said Melville has come home.

The young man named Brenton ran to the front of the library and out the doors and before Sam could move, he had scooped him up and carried him back inside. Right past the hedge where Chips was waiting, so he saw everything. Chips was in shock; he couldn't think and was frozen in place.

Inside the library there was another reunion. The Library Lady was still there. The woman who had adopted him as the library cat, who cared for him and fed him, the same person was be-hind the Main Desk—he would have known her anywhere. Her hands were on her cheeks and she was shaking her head in dis-belief. Brenton put Sam on the counter, and he slowly walked toward her and then sat down. There were tears on her face as she reached out to touch him. She began to rub his head and face like she always used to, exclaiming about the backpack, while staring into the green eyes in amazement. The Library Lady and Brenton were laughing and talking, and soon the commotion was noticed and a small group of people gathered around. Many re-membered him, and despite their shock, they were all so happy to see the long-lost Melville.

It was a homecoming the green-eyed cat could only have dreamt of.

Then, amid the greetings, Sam suddenly remembered. *Chips.* Chips was outside, where he left him. He had to be. With his heart pounding, Sam jumped down from the counter and ran to the front glass doors, crying and pawing at the door. Everyone was watching. This was so unexpected—why would he want to go back outside?? Brenton walked over to him, looked into the intelligent face and then back at The Library Lady, who nodded. So, he opened the door and followed Sam back outside. Sam went straight for the hedge, diving under it, and there was Chips, huddled down, quite wet (and very worried). Brenton reached down and gently picked up the small dapple dog, shaking his head upon seeing another backpack, and he carried Chips back to the entrance while holding the door open for Sam.

It was something to see. The library cat strolled in first. He made his way between the people, heading for the Main Desk (his question-mark tail in perfect form), and hopped up on the count-er. Sam sat down and watched as Chips was carried into the library

by Brenton, who gently placed the dapple dog next to him on the counter.

Together, Samuel Adams, also known as Melville, and Mr. Chips, also known as Chips, sat on the Main Desk of The Berkshire Athenaeum, backpacks still in place, having arrived at their final destination a little wet, but otherwise *safe and sound*.

The library closing hour was stretched quite a bit, as this was an amazing event and people naturally wanted to linger. It had not gone unnoticed they were both wearing ID tags, and when Brenton read aloud the tag information, the fact that they belonged to someone in Connecticut had caused the assembled group to gasp, collectively. Some wanted to open the backpacks, but The Library Lady said no, that should be for their owners to do. Finally, she had to shoo everyone out, telling them she would call the *Berkshire Eagle* first thing in the morning.

The local newspaper was certainly having a run of animal interest stories. The same reporter and photographer would be covering this story as Henny Penny Farm. And it would have been the lead story on the NATIONAL NEWS had they known this same cat and dog were hidden inside the famous chicken coop. Much less that the architect of the coop fortification was the cat formerly known as Melville.

After everyone finally left, The Library Lady and Brenton discussed what should be done.

"Samuel Adams . . . I already like the new owner. Melville is now a Founding Father!" Brenton was smiling as he looked at the cat's ID tag.

"And what a darling name, Mr. Chips, for this sweet little dog. I love that movie, *Good-bye, Mr. Chips*," The Library Lady said, smiling at Chips as she looked at his tag.

Both Sam and Chips were now quite relaxed (and dry), lying down on the counter. Chips was glad to be indoors and The Library Lady was very nice. She liked his name (and she had said something about getting them dinner soon).

"Number Thirteen Rabbit Hill Road, New Milford, Connecticut . . . it sounds so nice, out in the country, I would guess . . . do you think we should call the number right now?" The Library Lady asked, rubbing the tag in her fingers, thinking.

Sam and Chips exchanged a look of disbelief. Everything was happening faster than expected.

"Well, I'm sure it's a call they can't wait to get and will not believe . . . but it's late for them to drive here and back the same night, and the weather's pretty bad. Why not wait until morning? These two probably need a good night's rest. I can't imagine how they got here by themselves all the way from Connecticut. I wonder how long it took them . . ." Brenton whistled under his breath, shaking his head.

"I know, Brenton, if they could only talk!!" the Library Lady exclaimed, still amazed at what had happened.

A knowing look flew between Chips and Sam.

"I agree, one more night won't make a difference. I'll call them first thing in the morning, before I call the *Eagle*. You'll be here in the morning?" she asked, knowing he used the library as his office.

"Definitely, and I want to meet the new owner. Do you think they have any idea their cat once lived here?" Brenton asked.

"I don't see how they could. From the day he disappeared, I felt so guilty for not having ID tags on him. That he was not returned was my own fault. And I have never stopped worrying about what happened to him. If I had to guess, someone took him when he was outside, maybe thinking he was abandoned. People come from a distance to visit the Melville Room. Anyway, to know at last that he's alive and well is simply . . . wonderful . . ."

The Library Lady paused, studying the mysterious cat.

"Of course, now that I see him again, I wish he would stay . . . I could never bring myself to get another library cat. I always knew he was special. There would only be one Melville."

Now the looks exchanged were deep with meaning. *No new library cat.*

Chips was no longer hungry. Instead, he felt a gnawing sense of loss, like watching something drift away that you don't want to lose, but cannot get back.

"I know. I've thought about him while I've been working from here. It's nice to have a cat around a library. Well, I'll see you in the morning . . ."

"See you then, Brenton . . ." The Library Lady paused, remembering. "Time has flown by. I can still remember seeing Melville stretched across your high school books . . . and soon you'll be getting your own office. I will miss seeing you, but I'll stop by and visit . . . it's easy to remember a business named after a compass setting, true north. As Stuart Little said, north is a very good direction."

She studied him, the fondness in her eyes and voice apparent.

Brenton grinned and slung his laptop case over his shoulder.

"*Thank you* for being here and for always helping me, and everyone else . . . good night, *Melville* and Mr. Chips . . ."

He waved as he went out through the familiar doors.

Chips heard the name resonate like an echo, *Melville*, *Melville*.

The Library Lady drew in a deep breath with tears in her eyes. It had been an unexpectedly long and emotional day.

"Okay, young men. I'm running to the store for a few things and I'll be back with dinner in ten minutes. Don't let anyone in while I'm gone. The library is closed for the day, even if some lights are still on!"

She smiled, put them down on the floor, and was off.

In the short time she was gone, Sam quickly explored the Melville Room (unchanged) and other favorite haunts, happy to find everything pretty much as he remembered, which he reported back to Chips, (who nodded, but with no enthusiasm). Nothing else was said between them, and soon The Library Lady returned. The grocery bags held food, dishes, and a single pet bed. She gently took off their backpacks and told them they would sleep in the Melville Room, then put the food and water in bowls and set down the small bed. Next, she opened a door in the Melville Room and emerged holding another pet bed. When she set it down, Sam immediately stepped in, clearly pleased. It was obvious The Library

Lady had never given up hope that one day her Melville would return. As Chips watched, his heart felt even heavier. They both ate their dinners, but Chips ate slowly and did not eat all the food *or even lick the bowl.* Then she took them outside for a quick walk before bed. She stroked them both, turned off the light, and said she would see them in the morning.

Sam was happy and fell asleep quickly. Given his surroundings, it would have been a good guess that he dreamt of seafaring trips . . . and a white whale.

Chips looked around the unfamiliar room and sighed. Tears welled up again. It took him a long time to fall asleep.

No rooster awakened them, so they slept until The Library Lady woke them.

Chips had slept fitfully. As he woke up, he tried hard to think about seeing Mr. and Mrs. S. again and *nothing else.* They ate breakfast (Chips, again, not hungry), then took a quick morning walk, and were once again allowed to sit on the Main Desk counter. Chips liked this vantage point. Being short had its obvious disadvantages, so it was nice being at a height to look people in the face. *A lot* of people were piling through the doors as the library opened. Finding books to read or doing research never resulted in this amount of traffic at nine a.m.—it was obvious the news had travelled fast from those in the library the night before. Brenton was one of the early birds, and a little later the *Berkshire Eagle* reporter and photographer arrived. Photographs were taken and then The Library Lady and Brenton were interviewed (and the newspaper staff said they would stay for "the reunion," of course). Their backpacks were also put on display and photographed. Some people tried to open them, but the Library Lady was very quick to say they were PRIVATE PROPERTY.

What neither Sam nor Chips had been privy to was the telephone call to Number Thirteen Rabbit Hill Road. Mrs. S. had answered the phone in her "death's door" voice (which had become her normal tone of voice, prompting Mr. S. to tell her more than once that she did not work at a funeral parlor, to which she would reply that was the only place she could work because everyone was sad all the time at those places, and then she would usually burst into tears). But seconds after answering this call, she was screaming and whooping and jumping up and down and crying like a fountain (this is an accurate description). Mr. S. (and Bud) were *very* worried at first, thinking she had finally gone completely crazy, but as she got the words out that Mr. Chips and Sam Adams were *safe*, the roof of Number Thirteen came off (well, almost). And if Mrs. S. had driven, let's say, quickly from the airport on that terrible day, this time she had jet propulsion. The tires left the road for most of the drive to the Berkshire Athenaeum.

In record time (a record that would probably hold for all time), Mrs. S. pulled into a handicapped parking space (it was closest to the front doors), giving Mr. S. a look which he understood and agreed with. She had been emotionally handicapped from the moment they went missing, and so had he. They both leapt out of the car and ran into the library, and came to an abrupt stop. There they were, lying down on the library counter, looking relaxed and comfortable, healthy and not hurt, as good as they had always looked living at Number Thirteen. Mr. and Mrs. S. walked slowly toward Sam and Chips, staring in some disbelief. They had not talked about what to expect, but shared an unspoken fear their beloved pets would not look good (even though The Library Lady had reassured them on the phone both appeared to be just fine).

Chips nearly flew off the counter (a height not safe for a dachshund to jump), but luckily Brenton reached him just before he leapt and put him on the ground. Mrs. S. knelt down and he was in her arms in seconds. His body wriggled in every place, he kissed her over and over, and his tail did not stop moving. Chips had never felt such pure happiness as this moment. Then the same greeting for Mr. S. Tears, like rivers, ran down two faces. Mrs. S. slowly stood up, carrying her Chips, and walked toward Sam Adams, who looked like he always did, calm and cool. She gave Chips to Mr. S. and swooped up the green-eyed cat, who did not seem to mind all the affection.

The photographer captured the first moments of the reunion, and then they all sat down at a large table behind the Main Desk to be interviewed. Chips was in Mrs. S.'s lap and Sam lay down in the middle of the table. It was as if he knew he would soon be the center of attention. With a great deal of patience and gentle questioning, the reporter eventually obtained a coherent (non-emotional) accounting of what had transpired about a week ago at Number Thirteen Rabbit Hill Road. And just when he thought he had it all down, The Library Lady brought over the backpacks, and Mrs. S. became a water fountain (again). During the time the reporter was asking Mrs. S. questions, Chips was not listening. He was watching Sammy intently and thinking only about what his decision would be. So he never heard what actually transpired at Number Thirteen after the Great Escape. (And that was for the best.)

Looking at the two backpacks, Mrs. S. had to accept what the evidence had clearly indicated from the beginning: their escape had been *planned*. As The Library Lady and Brenton began talking about Sam's former life as Melville, her tearful gaze settled on the mysterious cat she thought she had known, but realized she did not. Her eyes reflected waves of emotion—awe, disbelief, amazement, shock, sadness, happiness, love, loss—it was like watching the sea change in a storm. What had happened was beyond comprehension. And there was so much that was not known, would never be known. Mr. and Mrs. S. both sat very still, not talking, and silence soon settled around the table.

It was the reporter who finally broke the silence.

"Well, I have the headline, 'THE INCREDIBLE JOURNEY.' Our readers are not going to believe this, and right after the miracle at Henny Penny Farm. If only they could talk, what a tale they would tell! All the way from New Milford, Connecticut, to Pittsfield, Massachusetts!! One cat and one dog, all alone, *with backpacks*!! And they made it. It's unbelievable. This is going to hit the AP wire and you are all going to be celebrities . . ." the reporter said, shaking his head over and over again.

Sam and Chips both heard "Henny Penny Farm" and "*celebrities.*" Sam winked once at Chips.

Chips thought he would feel happier about being a celebrity, but he didn't. He just wanted to know what Sammy would decide, and it was now so close he could hardly stand it. He wanted it over.

"So, my job, as a reporter, is to ask about the backpacks—can we open them now? Our readers will want to know what they took with them. And maybe it'll give some clues about how they managed to make this journey?" the reporter asked, hopefully, looking at Mrs. S.

Mrs. S. was in deep thought, but she had heard him. She slowly turned to the reporter and without saying anything, shook her head no. He looked disappointed, but nodded his head, respectfully. Brenton was watching The Library Lady. She was studying Mrs. S. and he could see she silently approved of the decision.

Then it was time for Mr. and Mrs. S. to leave. Mrs. S. had not spoken since it all became clear, the truth about Sam's background and the journey they had made so he could return to the library. As she stroked Chips lightly, The Library Lady picked up Sam, and Mrs. S. gazed thoughtfully at the older woman holding the gray and black cat.

"If Sam risked his life, and that of Chips, to find his way back here, this must be where he wants to live. Here at the Berkshire Athenaeum."

Mrs. S. dropped her eyes for a moment and took a deep breath, and then she looked up into the cool green eyes. "Sam, you should stay here if that is what you want. We will all miss you terribly . . . it won't be my three musketeers anymore . . ." Mrs. S. paused and smiled sadly. "But you, and you alone, must decide. Samuel Adams and Melville are equally good names for a brilliant cat."

Chips began to tremble in her arms, and she felt it and hugged him hard, whispering that she understood and that it would be okay, Bud was waiting at Number Thirteen. But her voice was catching and tears filled her eyes. It would not be all right. She knew this and so did Chips.

"I think the only way to find out what he wants is for Sam, or Melville, to choose . . . by walking to whom he wants to be with. If you will stand at that end of the table, I'll stand at this end," The Library Lady suggested gently, as she put Sam down in the middle of the long table. Given how smart he was, they all assumed he would understand this was the time to make his decision. And, of course, he did.

Mrs. S. gave Chips to Mr. S. and she stood at one end of the table. Chips could not look and buried his head in Mr. S.'s chest, still trembling and feeling like his heart would break if Sam did not choose them.

Sam sat, calmly. He looked at each of them. Then he stood and turned. *To The Library Lady.*

Melville walked slowly toward her and sat down.

Mrs. S. could not help the sob that escaped from her throat, and hearing it, Chips knew, and dug his head deeper, tears running down his dapple face. What he had feared, from the moment he knew why Sam wanted to return, had happened.

They left quickly.

The backpack with Chips' name was picked up and they were out the doors of the Berkshire Athenaeum. Mr. S. was driving home. Mrs. S. held the trembling Chips in her lap, trying hard not to cry, but the tears came like a flood. As the car pulled out of the handicapped spot, Chips jumped up and began whimpering, looking over her shoulder out the rear window of the car. He was trying desperately to get over the seat. Very reluctantly, Mrs. S. lifted him into the back seat. Chips stood with his front paws braced on the back seat, whimpering and crying, as he watched the library recede from view.

And then something happened.

Someone came running out the front doors of the library, waving madly. Holding something.

Chips immediately began barking frantically, and Mr. S. slowed down and then stopped, looking in the rear-view mirror.

The person kept running toward them. It was The Library Lady, *with Sam in her arms*, holding his backpack and what looked like a folded piece of paper.

Mr. S. put the car in reverse and backed up slowly, and soon she was standing at the front passenger window of the car.

"He changed his mind, I could tell—he was pacing back and forth and then jumped up on a small table where we have information about local tourist attractions and he pulled out this brochure with his teeth. I don't know what it means, but it has to be something important . . . then he became frantic, jumping up on the front doors and crying loudly, it was obvious he wanted to go with you," The Library Lady said breathlessly, as she handed the brochure to Mrs. S.

It read, "*Visit Tanglewood ~ Summer Home of the Boston Pops.*"

The Library Lady gently handed the gray and black cat to Mrs. S. (along with his backpack), leaned in and kissed him on the head, and told him if he wanted to visit again to *please come with his owners by car*. She smiled at Mr. and Mrs. S. with teary eyes, then turned and walked back to the library.

Mrs. S. slowly shook her head at the cat sitting in her lap. As if by magic, the tears running down her face were no longer sorrow-filled. Looking into the green abyss of his eyes, she knew Samuel Adams would remain unknowable and his extraordinary intelligence would never be understood. But she also knew all that mattered was he had chosen *them*.

Then she gently lifted Sam over the front seat and set him down next to Chips.

The car began moving. Chips felt weak from emotion and couldn't speak. He had never been so sad and so happy in such a short period of time. Sam sat like a statue, his striped tail wrapped snugly around his body as he studied the dapple face, and then he looked out the window. His voice was just a whisper.

"When I left Number Thirteen, I never expected to return. I knew it would be hard on you, Chips. And I hoped you would understand—that I was going home, back where I belonged. It was not my choice to leave the library, as you know."

Sam was looking at the sky, thinking about that fall day many years ago. Then he turned to look at Chips.

"What I did not understand is the difference between living somewhere and having a family. At the library, I belonged to everyone . . . and to no one. As I watched you leave with Mr. and Mrs. S., I finally understood . . . what I was about to lose I would never find again . . . *my family*."

Then Sam lay down, his long front paws stretched out in front of him, his green eyes a tranquil sea. At times, he could look sphinx-like, wise and strong, and that was how he looked at this moment.

Chips lay down on the seat, his gaze fixed on the regal face, now aglow in a shaft of light.

Sammy was the sun.

And Chips was once again orbiting the brightest star in his universe.

Knowing with absolute certainty there had to be a reason, Mr. S. charted the return trip to pass by Tanglewood, which he announced with some fanfare. It could not be seen from the front seat, but one dapple passenger levitated for a split second. Then Mrs. S. opened the brochure and said she would "double-check the directions," to the great relief of both back-seat passengers.

A hot midday sun was shining down as the car door was opened.

They were parked in a deserted parking lot at Tanglewood. Mr. and Mrs. S. watched as two small figures bounded out of the car and onto the lawn and ran to the edge of the woods, where they disappeared under a large flowery bush. Their eyes met, shining with curiousity and wonderment.

Moments later, one dapple dachshund emerged from under the bush with an orange and white striped monkey in his mouth.

And he pranced and he danced and he hopped like a rabbit, his tail waving like a high-flying flag.

Followed by one cool cat, whose question-mark tail was now asking . . . *when is the next adventure?*

EPILOGUE

Life at Number Thirteen Rabbit Hill Road slowly began to return to normal.

"Normal" is an interesting word—not very exciting and some might even say boring. As in: "Normal weather for this time of year" (ho-hum unless it's a Snow Day). Or, "His hearing is perfectly normal" (obviously, the audiologist did not study selective hearing in audiology school). Normal can also mean doing the same thing regularly and being lulled into the expectation that things will keep going the same way, day after day, week after week, month after month, year after year.

It is only when routine falters, stops dead in its tracks, and changes in a way that is *not good* that the pricelessness of normal is understood. Then you would give anything—anything—to get it back, and you would never stop feeling grateful if by some miracle you did.

And so it was for the residents of the rambling colonial house at the end of the dirt road.

Celebrating, *and not ever taking for granted again*, the little things that happen every day. Like sharing the bottom of the yogurt cup and the cereal dish with all interested parties. The morning walk with Mr. S., Chips taking the lead. Sam on his rounds, last stop Mrs. S.'s Studio, where the clacking had resumed with great zeal and catnaps never felt better. Bud never wavering from his strict schedule of eat, sleep, repeat. Mr. S. dispensing a small mountain of cat treats every afternoon (except on weekends when Mrs. S. was around). New Christmas sweater photos of the three musketeers (two *very* unhappy, one thrilled). Chips once again sleeping with Mr. and Mrs. S. (the others given an open invitation, but preferring their own haunts). Sam and Chips back at their posts on the window seat, the official observers of squirrels, birds, the change of seasons, and life in general at Number Thirteen.

There were a few minor changes.

No more Business Meetings, no more Vacations (for a very long time anyway, and even a moratorium on Weekend Trips), only health-related visits to the Vet, more tennis balls than a tennis camp, more toys than ever (celebrities do get a lot of free stuff), a large trunk to hold all the new toys (accessible to the short-legged toy owner by climbing a small stepstool, the better to survey one's realm), and more visits into town, where Samuel Adams and Mr. Chips were bona fide local celebrities. Chips found out that he *loved* being a celebrity. It was better than he could have possibly imagined. (And this status did include *free ice cream*, even in his hometown—he *really* wished he could tell Rockwell.) Sam was, let's just say, cooler toward the throngs of admirers. Not uncommon for those who have had prior experience with fame.

Mr. Chips carried Monkey Business around as much as ever (maybe more), still the one and only *most* favorite. The dozen or so new monkeys who looked suspiciously identical except for color, who had somehow managed to find their way into the trunk (??), were quickly relegated to "cheap imitation" status and never chosen for play dates. Chips' conviction that he could never live without his Monkey Business remained absolute, as was his acceptance that he might be stuck forever in the age of innocence. And this was *just fine* with him.

The two backpacks had been unpacked by Mrs. S. with a mixture of curiosity, trepidation, and tears. (Not in equal parts.) In Chips' backpack she found one of her scarves, one bone, *and a small black bowtie*. She studied the bowtie, mesmerized and utterly mystified—why would this be in his backpack and where possibly would he have worn it?? Then she held the scarf to her nose, breathing in the faint smell of her perfume . . . and something else.

Hay.

Her scarf had been somewhere where there was *hay*. Her mind wandered, as it had so often since they returned. Had they stayed in barns? What did they eat? How had they traveled seventy miles with apparent ease and safety? *Why had they gone to Tanglewood*— someone must have taken them, they could not possibly have stumbled upon it. She knew their journey would remain a mystery for the rest of her life. But she would never stop wondering where they had been, how they had gone such a great distance, and most of all, *who had helped them.*

Sam's backpack held a cat treat bag (curiously, not empty) . . . and *Mr. S.'s compass, a black bowtie, and a map with two large red X's, one near Number Thirteen and the other near Pittsfield.* She had held the map in trembling hands, studying the familiar route in disbelief, the facts indisputable: Sam had planned their trip *just like a person would, using a map.* (Mr. S. had whistled under his breath while shaking his head when Mrs. S. showed him the compass, map, and two black bowties. There was only silence and long looks between them. Definitely a bad case of "cat's got your tongue." Sam Adams being the cat.) Mrs. S. decided they shouldn't share the map or the other contents of the backpacks with the media (and she had been pestered by so many of those inquiring newspaper types—they were RELENTLESS). However, she could be one tough cookie when she had to be, and this was going to remain Top Secret. Sam and Chips were already famous for having made the long journey on their own, but the contents of their backpacks would remain private.

Sam's genius had to be protected.

It was also true that Mrs. S. had a pretty good imagination, being a writer. So, it wasn't hard for her to imagine some uniformed military muscleman from the CIA or FBI or some Secret Animal Research Center, coming to Number Thirteen and pounding on the door, holding a cat carrier made with titanium bars, and demanding to take possession of her Einstein Cat for Research, Brain Scans, or Something Else That Would Be Terrible. Inasmuch, it was not surprising she decided to stow both backpacks (with their contents) in the far reaches of a very high closet shelf (and inside a locked suitcase) when no one was looking (after midnight when everyone was asleep). Safely out of reach of the inquiring (nosy) reporters and Sam Adams—he who could never be tempted by the travel bug again. *Ever.*

Interestingly, it was determined after some steady observation that the cat door could be left open (no barricade was necessary), because only Sam would use it. Chips was content to come and go through regular doors on his leash, and Bud, of course, never left the softest spot he could find or the food dish. When they had arrived back at Number Thirteen, Bud's yellow eyes had blinked open and then widened in surprise upon seeing the two wayfarers. He had actually looked relieved to see them, and told them Number Thirteen had turned into something called a funeral parlor (according to Mr. S.), and even though he didn't know what that was, he said it was *definitely not* a place you wanted to live in. Chips was so thrilled to see Bud again, and immediately began telling him all about the Grand Tour. However, it was not long before Bud became impatient, confused, and sleepy listening to all the extraneous details, names, and places, finally telling Chips he just wanted to hear about *the food.* There was a lot to tell about this subject, so the storyteller happily obliged and exuberantly recounted this part of the tour. *One can only imagine* Bud's reaction when he found out what he had missed at . . . Katnip & Bonz.

Yet, even with time, the memories of the Grand Tour did not fade.

Lying on the window seat together, they often reminisced. Sam and Chips both missed (almost) everyone they had met, even Ziggy. There were happy, funny memories, and other times when the silences were long because the missing was hard.

Sam Adams had returned home with memories that would last a lifetime. Nevertheless, there were moments when he heard the beckoning call of the open road, and he could once again smell the fragrant summer air and feel the wind in his face as they headed . . . just around the bend. Then his gaze would fall upon a dapple face. Chips. *His best friend. His family. Number Thirteen was his home.* And the siren call of the open road became muffled, fading away like sleigh bells going deep into wintry woods.

Chips missed everyone he had met on the Grand Tour, so much that it made his heart hurt. More than anything else, he wanted to see them again. There was, however, one thing that made the sadness bearable. Something he knew was true. *They were all his friends, and they would be, forever.*

Thus, it was not surprising that the faces and voices of Star, Beeeeeezly, Buttercup, Dolores, Rockwell, Fenway, Ziggy, Devyn, Tweety Bird, Sir Lancelot, Mrs. Cluck, Mrs. Hunt-n-Peck, Mr. Farmer, Brenton, and The Library Lady often appeared in the dreams of one dapple dachshund and one gray and black cat.

And if you leaned in and listened closely, you might have heard these whispered words, carried in the gossamer threads of sleep, spoken between two dreamers . . . still looking for the rainbow's end.

"How about another Grand Tour, Chips?"

"Only if I can bring Monkey Business."

"Deal."

EPILOGUE

Here the teller of this tale of tails takes her leave.
When longen folk to go on pilgrimages (on four paws or two),
May the journey be *fantastic* and the homecoming sweeter still.

CAST OF CHARACTERS (STARS)

THE FOUR MUSKETEERS

Samuel Adams (aka Sammy or Sam) . . . . As Himself

Mr. Chips (aka Chips) . . . . As Himself

Bud (just Bud) . . . . As Himself

Ziggy (aka Zigbottoms, Zigmeister, His Hineyness) . . As Himself

Map of The Grand Tour
Route 7 and Local Environs

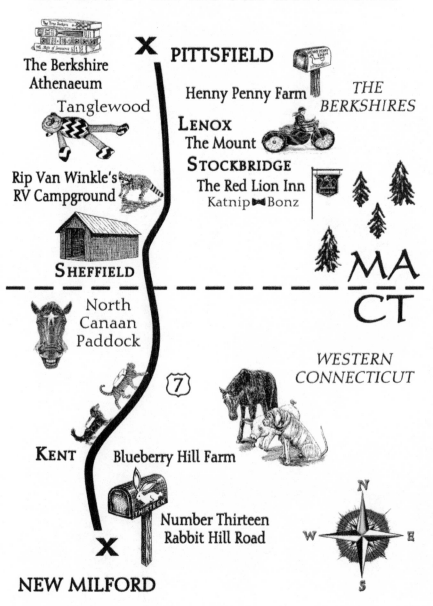

The Berkshire Athenaeum

Tanglewood

Rip Van Winkle's RV Campground

SHEFFIELD

X **PITTSFIELD**

Henny Penny Farm

LENOX
The Mount

STOCKBRIDGE
The Red Lion Inn
Katnip ▰ Bonz

THE BERKSHIRES

MA
CT

North Canaan Paddock

⑦

WESTERN CONNECTICUT

KENT

Blueberry Hill Farm

Number Thirteen Rabbit Hill Road

X

NEW MILFORD

N
W E
S

ABOUT THE AUTHOR

D. A. Squires is the author of *The Time Seekers*. *The Fantastic Tails of Sammy and Mr. Chips* is her second novel for readers of *all* ages.

She was inspired to write this story by the four-legged loves of her life. Their personalities, relationships, idiosyncrasies, and shenanigans were, quite simply, irresistible material. And they seemed to know it was all about them. Mr. Chips, Sammy, and Bud kept Mrs. S. company (perhaps held hostage would be more accurate) until the very last word was written. Sheriff Ziggy joined the posse whenever he rode into town (the shiny gold star attached to his collar was hard to miss), his clipboard full of "story ideas." Mrs. S. was actually besieged with unsolicited advice regarding plot and dialogue from all the stars. Sometimes she took their suggestions. But not always.

Writing the fantastic tales was the *joyride* of her life.

A graduate of the University of Connecticut with a Bachelor of Arts in English, *magna cum laude*, and elected to Phi Beta Kappa, Mrs. S. lives in Florida with Mr. S. (having previously lived in western Connecticut for many years), along with a steamer trunk of tennis balls and toys, cartons of cat treats, the one and only "Monkey Business," and of course . . . the musketeers.

DASquires.com

ABOUT THE ILLUSTRATOR

Kelly Arnold is an artist who specializes in commissioned portraits painted in oils. She has also created a compelling body of work called *Emotional Color*. Her artwork covers a spectrum of mediums including drawing, painting, sculpting, and computer graphics, and continues to grow.

She worked in the printing graphics industry for many years and then transitioned to creating and teaching art to students of all ages. Many of her students have won awards and developed into professional artists. Kelly is the founder of the Arts Enrichment Club. Through her many activities and online instruction, she works to inspire anyone with an interest in art to pursue their dreams.

The Fantastic Tails of Sammy and Mr. Chips is the second book she has illustrated and designed. The front cover artwork was done in oil and the sketches in pen and ink. She was the illustrator and graphic designer of the author's first book, *The Time Seekers*.

CPSIA information can be obtained
at www.ICGtesting.com
Printed in the USA
LVOW03*2250310118
564842LV00001B/7/P